SONGS & DITTIES OF THE FLEET

1st Edition

Published in 2012 by
Woodfield Publishing Ltd
Bognor Regis PO21 5EL England
www.woodfieldpublishing.co.uk

ISBN 1-84683-143-1

Printed and bound in England
Typesetting & page design by Nicolai Pastorius
Cover design by Klaus Berger

Songs & Ditties of the Fleet

A miscellany of maritime melodies & memorabilia

written and collected by

RICHARD BARR & BERNIE BRUEN

Woodfield

Woodfield Publishing Ltd

Bognor Regis ~ West Sussex ~ England ~ PO21 5EL
tel 01243 821234 ~ e/m info@woodfieldpublishing.co.uk

Interesting and informative books on a variety of subjects

For full details of all our published titles, visit our website at
www.woodfieldpublishing.co.uk

Dedicated to the memory of
Billy Seymour & Bernie Skuse

"We set a sail and see where it takes us.
We make friends and then we move on.
All we can do is remember as best we can."
Bernie Bruen

~ CONTENTS ~

About the Authors

Richard (Dickie) Barr

Dickie was born in 1941 into an Irish seafaring family (one of his ancestors served as Master at Arms with Nelson aboard HMS *Victory* at Trafalgar). The family sailed trawlers, first out of Brixham in Devon and early in the 19th Century moved to the river Liffey in Dublin. His father Andrew served aboard a cargo steamer belonging to the Ulster Steamship Company in the 1920s and related many stories of his life and times to his son. A sailors' life therefore, beckoned and after a dreadfully uninspiring state education he joined the Royal Navy as a Junior Seaman in 1958. During his career, both before and after qualifying as a Physical Training Instructor, he saw service in many parts of the world aboard a variety of ships, which included a landing craft, frigate, destroyer and two aircraft carriers.

It was during the latter part of his naval career that his friendship with Bernie Bruen was formed and the songs and verses in this book were written. Though not musically trained, Dickie taught himself guitar and piano accordion and created the melodies for many of the songs contained within this book. He was awarded the Meritorious Service Medal in recognition of long and dedicated service and retired after twenty nine years with the rank of Warrant Officer.

Upon leaving the service, he carved out a second career as a businessman and eventually as a consultant in business and human resource development, operating throughout the South West of England. Between 1991 and 2000 much of his effort was directed towards the states of the former Soviet Union, particularly the Ukraine. He is now retired and living quietly in the Sierras of Southern Spain.

NA (Bernie) Bruen

Son of Second World War naval fighter ace Commander J.M. Bruen, DSO, DSC, RN, Nigel Bruen – 'Bernie' to his many friends – was brought up in the naval tradition and with a deep love and appreciation of all things nautical.

He was educated at Wellington College and briefly flirted with the theatre before arriving at Britannia Royal Naval College, Dartmouth, as a cadet at the age of twenty-two.

Bernie specialised as a Mine Clearance Diving officer and in his spare time gained considerable experience in outward bounding, canoeing, boxing and other such robust pastimes. The common strand throughout his career was a love of music and an unerring ability to compose relevant humorous or poignant verse and ditties along the way.

After tours in Diego Garcia and on loan to the Sultan of Oman's Navy, Bernie was awarded the DSC for bomb clearance in the Falklands and, later, the MBE for mine clearance work in the Red Sea whilst in command of HMS *Gavinton*. Retired from the Royal Navy, he then served for ten years as Executive Officer of the sail training ship *Shabab Oman* in the Royal Navy of Oman.

He now lives quietly in rural France, where he keeps nothing more dangerous than chickens.

Preface

When I joined the Britannia Royal Naval College in 1968 as part of 39 Flight, we were encouraged by our Divisional Officer to purchase an anthology entitled *Flowers of the Sea*. In this book was to be found a host of authors and poets who had taken the sea connection as their subject. It is a wonderful volume and has been everywhere that I have, except perhaps to war – where for a short time we were much constrained in our choice of personal kit.

Now, after twenty-five years 'at sea', I feel that it is time to add a sort of unofficial appendix to the book by publishing and thus sharing my own views and feelings of that capricious environment. I thank 'Dickie' Barr for his contributions and help in producing the work and those anonyms whose words appear in the text. You all know who you are. There are references to various original tunes to the songs written. These are available separately from the authors, who would be glad to hear from anyone who is interested. Songs are for singing.

Inevitably a certain amount of history and various yarns and comments accompany the pieces. They all serve to enrich the basic fare and give insight to their origins. Some verse, the war poems, have already been published privately in the book Keep Your Head Down – A Falklands Farewell. They are reproduced here as part of the whole.

Here then is a small flower from a quarter century of writing and listening at and around the sea.

Bernie Bruen

1.   The Sailing Era

What follows, are songs and ditties written about the 'days of sail', in the times before the invention of the steam engine, when wind or oars were the prime movers of vessels upon the seas. They were the days when the sighting of another ship was heralded by a slanting rectangle of white on the horizon as the approaching vessel heeled to the wind. In those times, a column of smoke far away probably indicated a fire at sea or other emergency. Later, steamships were in the ascendancy but still scarce enough to cause comment and the majority of the world's trade was carried in wind-ships. Voyages of many months' duration culminated in rapid turn-around times in port and a swift departure on the tide.

The death knell for sailing ships occurred when the Panama and Suez Canals were opened making it easier and faster for steamers to compete on even terms. Only after sail had given way to steam, did those sailing ships that remained find themselves moored up in ports around the world for lengthy periods while shipping agents scoured the lists of export/import merchants to find them suitable cargoes. But throughout the sailing era, owners were loath to waste time that could more profitably be spent at sea; scarcely allowing any maintenance of the enormous rigging jigsaw and lengthy hull preservation which could only be done in harbour. Ships' captains knew that their jobs depended upon fast passages, the appearance of the vessel and their ability to reduce costs as far as possible. The ordinary working sailors were over-numerous and consequently poorly paid. Every berth was hard won and hard kept. These three factors came together to produce the singular practice of 'Ratlin'-down and Redding-up'. Reaching the higher latitudes of the 'roaring forties' and 'howling fifties' and the imminent passage of sailing ships around Cape Horn, meant the 'sending down' of fair-weather sails, spars and rigging, followed by the 'setting-up' of the heavier foul-weather gear. Once the Horn was rounded and the ships left the stormy southern oceans, the lower latitudes promised fine sailing, warmer weather and an easier life. When homeward bound, it was also a convenient time to carry out the maintenance so essential to the ship's safety and efficiency. The weather was equitable, days lengthy and the wind constant. The crew could be kept busy and, if busy, happy.

'Ratlin'-down', was the process of skimming off the old paintwork and removing rust, as well as taking down old and worn rigging that could be dangerous if left to weaken further. There were no synthetic fibres in those days and ropes made of natural products were prone to rot and fatigue. The ship would echo with the sounds of chipping hammers and scrapers as the bare metal was exposed and rust banished. Men, perched high in the rigging, painstakingly splicing new ropes into place, would stop awhile to watch the dolphin racing under the bow. Seen from the foremast t'gallant yard, such a sight could never be forgotten. Keeping perfect formation the dolphin would twist and weave, just beneath the cutwater as it rose and sank in the swell. The bowsprit's chain rigging and downward-bracing 'dolphin striker' would seem time and again poised to ravage those sleek and friendly shapes, only to be avoided, easily and lazily with a deft flick of the tail. 'Ratlin'-down' was a process eagerly looked forward-to by the sailors of old for, after the dangerous and often lengthy passage around the Cape, it was a time to relax and enjoy the pleasurable weather of the steady Southern Trade Winds. Whereas before, the watch could be called many times in the day or night to reef or shake out sails, ware-ship or heave-to, now life assumed an ordered simplicity and an easy routine.

No more the constant wet and cold, the biting wind and the mind-numbing gyrations of a precarious position aloft. No more the perilous struggle with frozen, snapping canvas and the danger of breaking seas and monster waves. Well at least not yet awhile.

Now was the time for 'Redding-up', the application of red-lead, Stockholm tar, pitch, grease, topcoat, boiled linseed oil and all the potions and concoctions that helped protect the ship from the assault of the elements. Dirty and smelly work to be sure, but there is a certain satisfaction to be had from slapping on a fresh coat of paint or smothering the steering chains in grease. It also meant applying a complete top coat of paint to all parts of the ship. So sailors would be perched on narrow wooden stages hung over the side painting, whilst the ship continued it's passage. This sort of task, coupled with the fine weather and contrasted with the previous harsh months, must almost have produced a holiday atmosphere on board. The first song, Ratlin Down, was written in unusual circumstances for it was composed while riding a motorcycle.

The reason that it survives at all is due to the continual halting of the accompanying van, 'Lenny' the Sheep Rescue Team wagon (that's another story), to dictate to the occupants each line or so as it occurred. It was a long trip but, a good song, to which Richard put one of his highly original and easily sung tunes.

RATLIN' DOWN

(Bruen/Barr) ~ Tune Original

Climb the rigging, spread the canvas
Now we've left the Horn behind us,
Now we've left the snow and sleet
Many leagues away,
Now we're in the South Atlantic,
Now that life is not so frantic,
We'll be redding-up tomorrow but,
We're ratlin-down today.

Now the Captain's sextant's brought us,
to the place the chart has taught us
That the weather's balmy and the sun is here to stay;
Now we have less cause to worry now that life is not a hurry,
We'll be redding-up tomorrow but,
We're ratlin-down today.

Now the dolphin play around us,
now the fairer weather's found us,
Now we'll make our clipper ship
as handsome as we may;
Now we'll make the paintwork ready,
now we're sailing homeward steady,
We'll be redding-up tomorrow but,
We're ratlin-down today.

Now we've got the Trades behind us,
Southern storms will never find us
Rolling home to England,
butting flying sheets of spray;
Studding sails are straining homeward,
dolphin striker bearing foamward;
We'll be redding-up tomorrow but,
We're ratlin-down today.

The whole period during which the modern square rigger, from tea clipper to the last of the big steel four and five masters, in all its multifarious forms and rigs, occupied a period of considerably less than a single lifetime. Yet it is estimated that 70,000 such ships entered the River Mersey alone in a single year. That is an average of 180 ships per day for one year, in one port in one country.

The number of sailing ships trading upon the oceans of the world during that time was legion. But, as sail inevitably gave way to steam, sailing ships disappeared with alarming speed. The last great sailing fleet was owned by that illustrious Finnish sea captain and ship owner Gustaf Erikson *(1872-1947)* of Mariehamn in the Aland Islands. There remains just one of his fleet, the four-masted barque *Pommern*, which is berthed alongside the jetty there and now open to the public as a reminder of far-off days, the ships and the men who sailed in them. Both Bernie and I, on different occasions, have visited this fine ship, to pay our respects to those who risked their lives whilst sailing them.

This song gives a small insight to the long-vanished realm of those ultimate wind-ships, whose records of sailing across the oceans of the world have never been equalled.

Perhaps a little explanation of terms would help those non-seafarers among you:

Shellback: An old salt or ancient mariner
Crimps: Boarding house agents and their runners
Nor'east fashion: The cheapest seamen's clothing available
The Downs; The English Channel off the Kent and Sussex coast
Half Deck: A midships deckhouse or tween deck, normally accommodating the apprentices and the galley
'Sails': A ship's sail-maker.

THE MIGHTY TALL SHIPS

(Dickie Barr) ~ Tune Original

Oh! the mighty 'Tall Ships' and graceful Clippers
That once sailed proudly on the breeze,
Their days were numbered like leaves of summer
And now they've all vanished from the seas.

The life was hard and the wages paltry
For those wretches that sailed before the mast
But there's many a Shellback will shed tears a-plenty
Now the days of the sailing ships are past.

Crews were procured in a state of drunken stupor
By the crimps who scoured sailor-town;
For a month's advance of pay they were clad nor'east fashion
And rowed aboard their ships in the Downs

With four boys in the half-deck and twelve men in the fo'c'sle
A cook, a 'sails', the Master and the mates,
They, watch and watch about, would work those grand 'Cape
Horners'
Over countless miles of lonely, watery wastes.

They brought Nitrates from Chile and took coal to Australia;
They raced to England grain and wool and teas
But Suez and the Panama and fast, steam-driven packets
All served to bring them swiftly to their knees.

Though their days have gone, the memory lingers
Of mighty windships trading 'pon the seas;
For the waves still remember the passing splendour
Of clouds of canvas billowing on the breeze.

Chorus:

The seas would rage and the winds would roar
As they sailed down to Rio and Cape Horn.
"All hands up aloft, lads. Take in the canvas
And we'll ride this gale out till dawn."

With the passing of the 'days of sail' and the advent of the technical age, many of the words germane to that by-gone era have passed out of our ken and into the specialised vocabulary of such groups as the Sail Training Association. Here they live on still. Such words and phrases, represented in this song, have a wonderfully evocative and salty air about them. They are from a language as pertinent to their subject as is modern computer speak and are as baffling to the layman as is a Cornish accent to a Scot. Ask the average sailor today to fetch a hand-spike and he will in all probability return with a small fid (a hand-held wood or metal prong, suitable for splicing rope and working shackles – although some would rightly contest this latter distinction). What you really wanted was a six foot long wooden spar with square section working end and a cutaway foot. Hand-spikes were originally used for training the ship's cannon onto the required bearing and now, in a similar manner to a crow-bar, for shifting anything heavy, like cable gear. The fid or marlin spike that the young sailor brought, does indeed fit nicely into the hand and is spike-shaped. This, together with the disappearance of the Lore of the Sea in these modern, high-tech times, would account for the arrival of the wrong piece of equipment. Not his fault – but perhaps ours for letting the old ways die. I wonder what the lad would make of such terms as 'handy-billy', 'joggle shackle' and even 'mollgoggah'. 'STRONGBACK AND PAWLS' is full of such terms – all parts of the rigging jigsaw of a windship. These would have been as familiar to the sailorman of old as 'bow-thrusters', 'self-tensioners', 'gyro stabilsers' and 'satnav' are to his modern counterpart. It is our intention to preserve in this song some of the better known words to add flavour and spice to a descriptive piece describing the life of the common seaman of the time, and to complement the song 'The Mighty Tall Ships'.

Both the tune and the arrangement which Dickie supplied to this piece are of wonderful ingenuity and tremendous fun to sing. To add further to your enjoyment, I have listed below some of the words that you may not have come across before:

Strongback: Large fitted wooden spar giving extra support to a structure.

Pawl: Fitting on a hand operated capstan which prevents the load from running back.

Vang: Rigging from the peak of the gaff.

Roband: A sennit plaited round head rope of a square sail.

Griping-Pad: Padding against which the gripes hold a seaboat.

Inner jib: Triangular sail set between the forestay and foremast.

Fore course: The largest square sail set on the foremast.

Yard: A spar secured to the mast to which a square sail, or sails, are secured.

Mainbrace: The largest piece of rigging in a sailing vessel.

Backstay: Standing rigging which supports a mast in it's proper position.

Martingale: Rigging which locates and helps support the jib boom.

Bobstay: Standing rigging from the forward part of a bowsprit to the stempiece.

Swifter: Rope fitted to slots in the outer ends of capstan bars.

Plain (sail): Corruption of 'Plain Sailing' – a simple operation.

Reef (sail): Reduction in the effective area of a sail.

Stun'sl: Abbreviation for Studding Sails, extra fine weather square sails.

T'gallant: Abbreviation for Topgallant – top or upper part of a mast.

Royal: Mast or uppermost square sails above the topgallant.

Trestle trees: Brackets on the lower masts to which topmast rigging is secured.

Cross trees: Athwartship spars on a mast.

Cleat: Metal or wooden fitting to which ropes are secured.

Salthorse: Salted Beef, normally stored in wooden casks.

Cro'jack: Abbreviation for Crossjack – the largest square sail on the mizzen mast.

STRONGBACK AND PAWLS

(Bruen/Barr) ~ Tune original

Inner jib, outer jib, fore course and yard,
Mainbrace, backstay and life that was hard,
Ice in your toe-nails and back burning raw,
No chance for the living and death welcomes all.

Martingale, bobstay, swifter and chain,
Sails struck down, reefed up or plain;
Rig stun'sl boom, t'gallant and royal;
Trestle trees, cross trees and boiled linseed oil.

The fight with the canvas, the wind and your fear,
The rigging to splice and the sails to repair,

The wind blows your lungs out, the waves snare your feet,
Your refuge the deck-house, your safety a cleat.

Hours spent aloft and more on the wheel,
Salt horse and beans for your 'vittles' every meal,
A half hour on Sunday was time of your own,
Three shillings a week for to send to your home.

The sea in your blood and the wind in your hair,
The cro'jack's a-cracking, no canvas to spare.
'Let fly!' shouts the Master, 'Before we are lost,
Or we'll founder this day to the Company's cost.

Chorus:

Remember the strongback and pawls, me boys.
Remember the strongback and pawls, me boys.
Your vangs may have twisted and your robands gone,
Your griping-pad split but life goes on.

Here is another delightful song. Today we would talk about 'culture-shock'. Then, I expect that the sailing man would have leaned on the pinrail, taken another pull at his pipe and merely shaken his head. This song spans both the sailing and steam eras and I have tried to depict the pride that sailing crews had in their ships, even though the work was hard and the hours were long. When the age of sail passed away, that pride all but passed away with it. *Dickie Barr*

COASTWISE

(Dickie Barr) ~ Tune original

Graceful lines, complete perfection,
Mirrored in sublime reflection,
The offshore mist doth proud unveil,
A sculptured pyramid of sail.

Buff and polish, scrub and scour,
Holystoning by the hour,
Swab and sponge, wipe and dry,
A finer sight can't meet the eye.

Spruce and natty, spick and span,
Before the wind our schooner ran.
Fresh and dewy, neat and tidy,
Standing off for Aberidy.

Then hove in sight a coasting tramp,
Besmudged with soot and smutty smoke,
Black and dingy, thick with dust,
An abhoration streaked with rust.

Bilge of squalid, festering grime,
Northward bound towards the Tyne.
Pollutes, defiles and desecrates,
The lonely sea it navigates.

Funnel stench contaminates,
Befouls the sky and ocean wastes.
Musty, fusty, cobwebby,
What evil mind invented thee?

THE PASSING OF THE MONTAGUE WHALER

There was a time when virtually every naval ship carried a Montague Whaler, and the boat meant everything to the Royal Navy. It was a lifeboat, stores-boat and landing craft; a recreational boat for banyans and picnics and used with much gusto as a racing galley under oars or sail.

When the Fleet held a regatta, it was a marvellous sight to see several of these craft pulling hell for leather down Grand Harbour, Malta, with oars bending under the strain. The cox'n stood in the stern-sheets, leaning forwards, to urge his crew to greater efforts. The 'all-comers' race, generated as much excitement among spectators, as would the closest run Derby. Protruding from the stern were two spare oars, for often one would break. Should this happen, then witness the display of faultless seamanship that ensued:

CRACK! Number Four's oar has broken and immediately he throws it up and away, clear of his port side crutch, (a rowlock cut into the gun whale) and clear of Number Two's oar.

SPLASH! and it lands in the water well on the port quarter of the speeding craft. The Cox'n grabs the spare oar from the port side and hauls it up above his head, the blade out to his left and the loom horizontal and athwartships. With a mighty heave, he throws the oar bodily over the heads of the straining crew -. straight into Number Four's upstretched hands The oarsman deftly catches the loom and in one flowing movement changes its direction of flight from forward to downward; steering it in its descent straight into the vacant crutch. Then, leaning forward, he sets the blade in the water and pulls in time with the rest. And how long did this take? Counting the strokes that occurred during this manoeuvre, he broke it on the first stroke and he rejoined the cadence on the third.

Probably the most demanding of Montague Whaler races was that of the 'Crash Whaler'. A measured distance would be divided into several equal parts and these parts rowed and sailed alternately. However, when pulling, the masts and sails had to be stowed inside the boat and when sailing the oars likewise. The trick was to work-up the six-man crew to make the transition in the quickest possible time and to keep way on the boat. Every man complemented the other and each task had to be done in the correct order and time. Again, the application of pure seamanship displayed on these occasions was a wonder to behold. You will not see such a sight again for these boats have all but disappeared and, where they still sail, they are lonely for a glimpse of their own kind.

As the Navy became more 'modern' in its thinking, so these beautiful craft were replaced by the impersonal and antiseptic fibreglass tubs that try to pass for their equals. But nothing could quite replace the Montague. No sailor in today's Navy will be seen lavishing upon his assigned boat the love and attention that the old Whaler engendered. Somehow the picture of five or six men setting off on a 'jolly' perched, wet-suited, on half a dozen Laser dinghies does not conjure up the cosy friendship of the more relaxed Whaler Banyan (picnic). Something has been lost in the transition from the simple fun of sailing one of these craft to the purely individual experience of the Laser. Everything becomes a race and no-one is content to just 'go sailing'.

But that is all they have got now, poor dears, so they will just have to make the best of it.

In the early seventies, when the 27ft Montagues and 32ft Cutters began to disappear from the Fleet, they were collected together and held in the old Boat Pound, just on the right as you enter Portsmouth Dockyard's old Main Gate. Looking down on these once immaculately kept boats was one of the saddest sights that one could imagine. Half full of water, halyards and rigging left flapping or hanging dejected down, gratings awash and stretchers awry, warped, hog-backed and dying, they lay there the casualties of someone's 'good idea'.

'For each man kills the one he loves. . .'

I awoke one night and wrote this song as it appears here, and not a word have I changed from that time. My good mate Shep Woolley was so struck by the song that he recorded it on his double, long playing record 'Goodbye Sailor', composing a haunting tune, admirably suited to his voice and presentation. I have heard it sung to the original tune and to Shep's in various places around the world and have sung it in many more myself. Some years later, my 'Sea Dad', Fiddler Jennings, and I managed to save one of the few surviving original Montagues from destruction. Fiddler refitted it and took many a person to enjoy its unique sailing experience. Called the Montague Swan, the Whaler is now living down in the Fowey area where she sails and takes part in the local Galley Races. We have heard of another original (without an engine) that sails somewhere on the East Coast. One day they might meet up, *inshallah*.

Meanwhile to whet your appetite, I include an apposite Tanka. (a Japanese verse form consisting of five lines, the first and third having five syllables, the others seven)

Montague Swan

Crafted by Shipwrights,
Sailed by heavy-handed men,
Your number, too old,
Discarded, I saved you – but
'Where are your vanished Sisters?

Montague Swan is actually a diminutive of her real name, that in itself was somewhat of a mistake. The very charming and lovely lassie who performed the official naming outside the Swan Hotel at Devonport, became a little confused at the moment critique and had to be hurriedly corrected. Hence, I suppose the real name of the boat should be as contained in the following extract from the ceremony:

'I name this ship Montague Whaler...'

'*Swan*, you idiot – Montague *Swan!*'

MONTAGUE WHALER

(Bernie Bruen) ~ Tune original

Your lacings are frayed and your sheets disarrayed,
Your traveller's jammed at the yard;
You've lost cringle and bung and your planking is sprung
And the grease in your pintle's gone hard.

Your garboard strake's split and your stretchers don't fit,
Your paintwork's beginning to peel.
Your gun'ls have dipped and your tiller's unshipped
And the deadwood's adrift from your keel.

They once sailed you proud, sang your praises out loud,
The pride of the ships that you served
But no more will they shout as they put you about.
Is this the reward you deserved?

Your legend's been told by the sailors of old
Of the lives that you saved from the sea.
You're the last Galliot. You've been left here to rot;
Now, who's goin' to save you for me?

When you shake out your reef, take the wind by its teeth
And sail into history and song,
Though we've thrown you away, please recall what I say,
'Forgive us for being so wrong.'

So away with your keelson, away with your yard,
Away with your mizzen and main,
For the days of the Montague Whaler
Are the days we will not see again.

SINDIBAD JIG

Tim Severin's voyage from Muscat in Oman to Canton in China
is a classic of its type. Retracing the steps of the most famous

Omani of them all, Sinbad the Sailor, he sailed in a very special boat – the *Sohar*.

This Dhow was built in the ancient way using traditional materials, on the beach at Sur, the old boat-building town to the south east of Muscat. No metal fastenings were used, for the vessel was lashed and sewn together using hand-laid coconut fibre ropes. Timbers, wedged between convenient rocks, were bent to shape by the natural progression of tide and sun. When *Sohar* came to the Muscat Naval Base for fitting out, I was lucky enough to be able to help out from time to time and was a frequent visitor. More important, though, I was onboard the day the sails were first hoisted and the crew, with many a 'stamp-and-go', did so to the strains of the specially composed Sindibad Jig; played on the violin that would later achieve fame as the Falklands Fiddle. (It now resides in the Port Stanley Museum in the Falkland Islands)

When I wrote the Sindibad Jig (after the *Sohar's* nickname), I did not know a jig from a reel in musical terms. Furthermore, I had then and have now little idea of how to write down music (however Danny Mullen has been kind enough to do it for me). Hardly surprising, then, that it is actually, and appropriately, a Hornpipe (or it could double as a march).

Bernie Bruen

Shanties were sung in order to synchronise the pulling or hauling effort of seamen. This is a short-haul shanty, specially written for hauling up the mainsail of a 'Lochen' Dory. There are no new shanties (or Chanties) anymore. They have been ousted from our high-tech world by the power winch and the donkey engine (that should bring back a few memories to the old Sea

Dogs); so we have got out of the way of working ropes by hand. But, come the fuel shortage or the electrical failure; come the mechanical breakdown or the computer malfunction, those ropes must still be hauled, the sails must be set and there is only ourselves to do it.

Perhaps this shanty will keep the old ways alive a little longer and maybe one day will come back into its own. Meanwhile, it is jolly good fun to sing – a real stamp-and-go.

SINDIBAD

Composed By Ferril Peurn.
Arr. Danny Weller.

Transcribed by CNW on Apple Mac
with Encore. January 12/93

JENNY IN THE MORNING

Tune original

You can be the Fiddler, I'll be the Chantyman,
Oh my darlin' Jenny in the morning,
Sitting on the capstan, standing on the foc's'l,
Oh my darlin' Jenny in the morning.

Fiddler's elbow, Chantyman tempo,
Oh my darlin' Jenny in the morning,
Sailors' halyards hoisting up the mainsail,
Oh my darlin' Jenny in the morning.

You play the melody, I'll sing harmony,
Oh my darlin' Jenny in the morning
Running down the half-deck, turn around the staghorn,
Oh my darlin' Jenny in the morning.

2.   The Age of Steam

My first 'proper' ship was the Type 14 frigate HMS *Hardy*. When she had boiler problems, the entire crew changed over to her sister ship HMS *Russell*. Like many others who served aboard these delightful little 1,400-ton frigates, I grew to love them beyond all others and indeed still do. Type 14s and the 'Tons', both classes of warship, have always held a strange fascination for those who lived in them and engendered the loyalty of respect and love.

This poem is how l said goodbye to *Hardy*. That was back in 1971, but she is still in my thoughts. It is a hard thing to say farewell to a ship but every time I read these words I am transported back to stand again upon her bridge and see her run.

Bernie Bruen

FAREWELL THE SHIP

(Bernie Bruen)

I know from whence you came, and how, and when.
I know not where you go, 'though that I care.
I only know that here you lie alone,
As though throughout your life
You had no time for rest, no time to spare.

To see you battle with the violent sea,
And watch you turn and quiver at my whim
Still fills me with a doubt that humankind,
Although so full of ken,
Could ever fashion such a dancing trim.

I wonder what you feel, small cockleshell.
I wonder how you suffer, little ship.
For 'though you do not live and breathe like me
Soon, in a time apart,
Your name shall evermore be 'at the dip'.

You feel so many move upon your decks.
You see so many boisterous and wild;
But is there somewhere in your mystic heart
A place for those you've held
Within you like a mother with her child?

When I am old and thoughts are faded grey,
My mind is cast to sailing broad and free,
So will I veer away from winds of death
To walk again upon
Your living decks, that float the timeless sea.

These Blackwood Class small frigates, of which HMS *Hardy* was one, were designed and built in the 1950s for the specific purpose of being used as convoy escorts, should a war occur. The concept was to produce simple, cheap, quickly built ships, carry out trials on them, put them in 'mothballs' and wait for the next conflict. Twelve of these frigates were built, all named after the captains of Nelson's ships at the Battle of Trafalgar. One, HMS *Palliser*, remained in preservation for some considerable time. In the 1970s she was released and achieved the aim of 'mothballs to operational' in six weeks. The rest were put to work, taking part in the first Cod War and being engaged on Fishery Protection duties, the Type Fourteens enhanced the reputation that these ships had, of being fine, if extremely uncomfortable sea-boats. They were also effective close-range submarine chasers.

One of their ablest exponents, and Captain of HMS *Hardy* and, following that, HMS *Russell*, was Lieutenant Commander 'Black Mac' Neil McLeay, who was one of the finest ship-handlers of his day. By the time this song was written, *Murray* and *Pellew* were long gone and most of the others too. But *Exmouth* was still there, the first gas-turbine powered warship in the world. Sadly, she is now but a memory. The Type Four-teens engendered great feelings of loyalty among their crews.

No matter that they were thrown about in heavy weather, nor that in similar circumstances, it was impossible to get hot food to the occupants of the after messdecks. No matter that they were narrow, wet and uncomfortable, nor that they were not particularly fast, nor that, with the 'Tons', they were the work-horses of the Fleet. They were well-loved ships and, lest they be forgotten, their story should be told – at least in part.

BALLAD OF THE TYPE FOURTEENS

(Bernie Bruen) ~ Tune original

The Malcolm and the Keppel shared the cold North Seas,
Pounded by their. anger, they watched the waters freeze
While Duncan sailed with Dundas in friendship side by side.
When one was sent to slaughter, the other quickly died.

The Palliser lay waiting in the silence of the 'trot'
To die the lonely death of the ship that men forgot.
That Grafton was the first to go, few men remember now,
And Blackwood was a training ship before her final bow.

The Russell and the Hardy always seemed to share the crews;
In going, they for many were the hardest ones to lose.
Let Exmouth sail forever, if Their Lordships it may please,
The last of the sprightly Type Fourteens,
The 'whippets' of the seas.

So look beyond the crashing wave,
The blizzards and the gales
And see them soar to legend,
With the Clipper Ships and Whales.

This next song is a Rant. It should be sung with gusto for it celebrates the existence of those same Type Fourteen frigates that did all that was asked of them, and more.

Uncomfortable they may have been but their 'sprightly movement o'er the sparkling sea', the way that they could 'turn and quiver at the slightest whim' made them special in so many ways. So don't let's be sad that they're all gone now. Get in there, sing this song, give it a bit of 'welly' and remember.

DRIVE 'EM DOWN IN A ROLLING SEA

(Bruen/Barr) ~ Tune original

Three hundred and ten from stem to stern,
Drive them down in a Type Fourteen
She'll kill with the grace of heel and turn,
Drive them down in a rolling sea
Slim and strong with a taste for speed,
Drive them down in a Type Fourteen
Unrivalled 'hunter' of her breed.
Drive them down in a rolling sea

Built by a nation's fear of war,
Drive them down in a Type Fourteen
For convoys that they never saw.
Drive them down in a rolling sea.
Sent to protect our fishing fleet,
Drive them down in a Type Fourteen
They served their time in snow and sleet,
Drive them down in a rolling sea.

The Landsman cried to Parliament,
Drive them down in a Type Fourteen
'Isn't it time these old ships went?'
Drive them down in a rolling sea
Parliament cried to the Admiralty,
Drive them down in a Type Fourteen
'For them we have no further need.
'Drive them down in a rolling sea!'

Grafton and Pellew were the first to go,
Drive them down in a Type Fourteen
With Murray and Blackwood soon in tow,
Drive them down in a rolling sea
Duncan, Malcolm and Palliser,
Drive them down in a Type Fourteen
No-one thought of saving her,
Drive them down in a rolling sea.

Dundas and Keppel without a care,
Drive them down in a Type Fourteen
Russell and Hardy within a year,
Drive them down in a rolling sea
So, if you've got a craving to,
Drive 'em down in a Type Fourteen,
There's only Exmouth left for you to
Drive 'em down in a rolling sea.

Originally a poem to say Farewell to the Blackwood Class frigate HMS *Russell*, the words were put to music by Dickie and Bernie (*Ratlin' Down*) in the mid-70s when they were singing the circuit around the South Coast and Portsmouth. Its haunting tune and sentiment was popular with audiences in the area for, just below the surface, there is a 'sailor' in us all. Years later, in Rosyth Dockyard, I came across the *Russell* awaiting disposal for scrap. It was as sad a sight, as was my last view of the *July*

Star, made all the more poignant as I remembered all the happy times on board. The lines from that 'Farewell' of twelve years before came into my mind:

> *So though they scatter all your bones,*
> *To four majestic winds and seven seas...*

It was then that I changed the title of the song to reflect the finality of what I saw.

THE SHIP DIES

(Bruen/Barr) ~ Tune original

Though in so short a time I must depart
To larger, ponderous beings unlike thee,
I never will forget your name or kind
Nor sprightly movement o'er the sparkling sea.

For though in years to come you will disperse
Your present form into a thousand ways,
Although I live a hundred years or more,
Your name will never, ever be erased.

For you are not contained like us
Into a self-employing grave
Where every deed and act is based upon
Self- importance and self- praise.

Unlike us humans, who can be ourselves,
You are made of more than forg-ed steel.
You do not just consist of iron and toil
But have a soul with an immortal seal.

So though they scatter all your bones
To four majestic winds and seven seas,
Your name and precious memory will e'er remain
With those you've sheltered in your lee.

You cannot be destroyed or left unknown.
You cannot be forgotten or outcast,
For old men talk and, when they walk no more,
Remember love they gave thee to the last.

Though in so short a time I must depart
To larger, ponderous beings unlike thee,
I will keep thee near me all my life,
Remember thee in whom I lived
And who still lives in me.

With their wide paddle wheels either side of the hull, their low superstructure and dismountable masts, *Paddlers* were the only tugs who could get under the flaring side of an aircraft carrier and have enough power to manoeuvre her correctly and safely. When seen turning under power, one paddle ahead, one astern, especially when viewed from the air, they had a majesty and a potency that only a Paddler can possess. Wherever carriers were likely to berth around the world, there would be found one or more of the Paddle tugs. Whether in Singapore, Malta, Gibraltar or Britain, they waited for the call; but, whereas once a line of those leviathans would stretch from horizon to horizon, now they are seldom seen and the Paddler's days are over.

Some waited out many years far away without a glimpse of their long-awaited sisters. Others languished in home ports, tending to those lesser warships that used to throng the dockyards. Occasionally there was a cruiser to shift but seldom their raison d'être. Now these words join the Dead Ships songs in remembering those we shall never see again. Their names are contained within the following song.

PADDLE TUGS

(Bruen/Barr) ~ Tune original

Your life was conceived, your power unbelieved,
Your purpose to serve whom it please.
Your very existence was gentle insistence
Of line to the Knights of the Seas.

You lay here and waited 'till their movement dictated
The stirring of 'fires' in your hold,
Then majestic white power you gave by the hour
As you stood by to welcome the Bold.

Then with gentle caress and with powerful address
You manoeuvred those giants' returns
And you'd fuss and you'd shove and when seen from above
You'd show off your beauty in turns.

But now you're reduced to providing the boost
To those ships that are scarcely your peers
And those masters you knew are so far and few
That you meet less and less through the years.

For you're dying my friend and the life that we lend
Can only prolong your demise;
So perhaps you should go where all faithful ships go
And sail evermore 'neath blue skies.

Yes – GRINDER, GRIPER, DEXTROUS you are called.
DIRECTOR, FORCEFUL, CAREFUL you have been,
Shepherding the carriers in and out of port,
Most FAVOURITE, FAITHFUL paddlers ever seen.

It was a clear, fresh morning in 1975 when the lookout aboard HMS *Bulwark* spotted the forward section of the Motor Vessel *July Star* adrift somewhere in the Mediterranean. The weather was calm and she wallowed in the slight swell as the operation to tow the wreck to safety was started by our helicopters and an

---

accompanying destroyer. There is probably no sight sadder to a sailor than that of a ship thus distressed, all the sadder because it transpired that a salvage tug had already arrived on the scene, snaffled the stern section and left. The stern contained all the valuable machinery and was worth much money to a salvager whereas the front end held no such treasure and had thus been abandoned to drift.

The surviving section of the hulk was towed by the Royal Navy to Gibraltar, where she was secured to the southern mole. She stayed there for some time before being moved to the centre mole, where she remained even longer. I never did find out how the *July Star* was cut in half, nor did I discover her eventual fate, but I remember how I first saw her and when, considerably later, I last saw her, blindly tethered to that outer mole.

There is always a terrible sadness in such a sight, the feeling that, deep inside, there lurks the soul of the ship, desperately crying for help and puzzled that no one seems to hear. Years later, I recalled that scene when boarding the still burning RFA *Sir Galahad* in Bluff Cove. I re-wrote the poem as 'The Derelict' to do honour to that gutsy old lady, but here is the original.

JULY STAR

(Bernie Bruen)

She lies as lies the rabbit or the doe,
With broken back and rapid, shallow breath,
Who rises even yet before its foe
And shouts defiance; shouts it unto death.

She lies and cries from pity and from shame;
Looks up to give a blind and helpless call

Whose answer echoes, calling out her name,
'No one will come. No aid arrive at all.'

She lies and sighs so lonely in the dawn,
Her bulkhead at the mercy of the tide,
Her lifeboats gone, their ladders left forlorn
Who slowly swing and scratch and scratch her side.

She lies and dies; she sees the waves advance
And waits to feel them wash her life away
Until the long, grey ships her pleas entrance
And softly come to help her on her way.

Bill Seymour was a much-loved folk singer whose mellow baritone and gentle sense of humour endeared him to many a heart. Founder of 'The Seymours' and later that most excellent collection of musicians, 'The Pheasant Pluckers', his music and memory live on, despite his death in the late 70s. To his funeral came folk from the length and breadth of the land and, at his Wake in the Greyhound Inn by Millbay Docks (alas no more) in Plymouth, so many people were gathered that music-makers had to stand on chairs and tables in order to be able to play.

Bill was brought up in the Docklands of Cardiff – in Tiger Bay itself – and later went to sea in the Merchant Fleet, seeing war service on the Russian convoys. A staunch supporter of the Royal National Lifeboat Institute, his music raised large sums for them, a tradition that those who knew him yet maintain.

A year or so before Bill died, he asked if I would write a song about his birthplace; to remind people of how it once was. We sat in the kitchen of a friend's house one day and he told me about that long departed lifestyle that was once normal in Tiger Bay. He told me how no one would ever lock a door; how neighbours would always help those in trouble; how children had a carefree world in which to grow up and play. Yes, they lived on the line of poverty but that only made families come closer together and interact the more with one another. He spoke mostly of the children; the games they would play; the scrapes they got into. He told how every year the police would gather them all at Lowden Square and select those who would be lucky enough to go on that year's outing to Lavernock. He told of the great ships that came to the port and how his seafaring grandfather would sit and smoke and watch their doings, spinning strange yarns to the open-mouthed youngsters.

He told of the fun to be had in and around the locks, stills and basins of the dockland and mused on the lack of work, the heartbreak and the hunger. He remembered 'The Man in the Car' – who owned the businesses and who could give out work and provide jobs – if he was suitably impressed. He remembered the bustle of the seaport, chock-a-block with steam ships, coasters, dredgers, sailing craft, tugs, barges, even huge liners that came for repair, but also the crowds of men on street corners, the depression, the charity, the hopelessness.

When Bill went back there, shortly before he died, he found it all changed. Many of the landmarks were gone, the industry had vanished and the docks were empty. Like looking at the thin ghost of a bustling past, here was all that remained of that once busy community. Yet the colours were the same and the children still played those games he once knew. Even now, so many years later, I can remember, vividly, sitting in that kitchen, listening to this wonderful man telling of his childhood, much as he himself must have listened to his grandfather outside the New Sea Lock Hotel. Somewhere I still have the notes I took, somewhere the original song I wrote – all twenty-eight verses of it. But here is the finished version, a song that Bill loved as he loved his childhood home of Tiger Bay.

TIGER BAY

(Bernie Bruen) ~ Tune original (Bruen/Barr)

*You'd run and watch the steamers
of the Campbells' Paddle Line
Come waddling into Weston, their white paint all a-shine.
You'd see the man from Ireland in the New Sea Lock Hotel
With his pipe and twist of 'baccy'
and you'd hear the tales he'd tell
As he watched the silent sailing ships,
the forests of their masts,
Of barque and brig and barquentine and memories of his past.*

*You'd sit and bath before the fire and do as you were told,
As you're the youngest, you're the last and dirty water's cold.
You'd play in all the doorways and sit the greasy pole,
Go every year to Lowden Square with Lavernock your goal.
You'd dive in competition when the lock began to fill
And chase away the swans and then, go swimming in the 'still'.*

*Your father's job had perished
and you'd stand to wait your turn
For free soup from the 'kitchen',
though for wholesome food you'd yearn.
You'd see your father waiting at the corner by the Bar
And you'd see him take his hat off
to the 'Man who drove the car';
And to Mount Stewart's graving dock
came ships from all the land
But your father still played pitch and toss
and you'd play sleight of hand.*

*But now the bridge has disappeared,
the canal has been filled in,
The docks disused, the houses closed*

and nothing's left within.
Campbell's Jetty's rotted.
Bute Street's been pulled down
And Lowden Square, where every year
you gathered from the town.
The smoke still stains the yellow brick, the kids are still at play
But only fading memories are left to Tiger Bay.

Tiger Bay, Tiger Bay, has your memory faded away?
Did it sail with the dredgers from Harrowby Quay?
Was it lost where they finally lay?
Was it lost where they finally lay?

THE NIMROD AND THE TERRIBLE STORM OF '77

It was the night of 14th November 1977 when HMS Gavinton was attempting to make the eastward passage around the Mull of Kintyre. She was slowly winning, butting into the very fangs of a storm force twelve coming t'other way. In all this dreadful weather, first the 'Gav' had been sent here, then there, then to another place; finally back around the Mull again, and all against the clock. 'You may be askin' why but you're gettin' no reply.' 'Twas Operational Secret.

Now, you cannot go very swiftly against a force 12 gale, not in any ship, excepting perhaps the long-gone HMS *Vanguard*, whose enormously flared bow gave her superb sea-keeping qualities. A 450-ton Minesweeper (a Hunter, actually, but it looked much the same as the Sweeper that we all used to know) can barely make headway against such a storm. Such were the steep seas sweeping past the Mull that speed was reduced to dead slow. Anything more would have shaken the guts out of her and rattled her poor old bones to crackling. As it happened, even dead slow was giving her one hell of a pasting and shaking the guts out of her crew. So 'dead slow' it was, and that on one engine only.

Normally this would have been a problem in itself for 'steaming' (or more accurately 'dieseling') dead slow for more than about fifteen minutes on the Deltic train engines with which these ships were fitted would produce the unpleasant side-effect of the funnel catching fire. It would roar like a volcano and a column of flame and brightly-burning soot-cinders would erupt from the stack like the full-boost afterburner of a jet fighter. The only remedy was to stop the engine quick, shut everything down and cool the funnel with hoses. In calmer weather we could have shut down the engine to allow the funnel to cool and so reduce the risk of fire, but this was far too dangerous in such a severe gale, as inevitably the ship would be swept onto the rocky cliffs forming the Mull of Kintyre.

But the Mull had to be rounded and the little ship plugged on. As it turned out, so much water was in the air from blown spume and spray or coming over the ship from the crashing of waves, that the funnel was being continually cooled and never had the chance of catching fire. We navigated the ship close by the shore in an attempt to reduce the distance to be covered and so make up for lost time. The Operational Objective came first. Finding the way round the Mull was not easy either.

The steepness and regularity of the seas, despite having their tops blown off by the wind, made the poor ship slam and judder to such an extent that it was all but impossible to read the chart. With but one shore light to go by and the radar jarred into submission by the furious gale, navigation came down to the old fashioned method of 'bearing, judgement, the seaman's eye and the Book of Psalms'. Young 'Sten' Stenhouse, the ship's electronic expert, alternatively buried his head in the radar's abdomen and consigned the contents of his abdomen to the 'head' (spew-bucket). But he persevered and was rewarded now and again with a fleeting glimpse of 'land' on the clutter-filled radar screen, before the machine wrapped its hand in yet again.

The Mull was rounded in six and a half hours of bone-jarring, eyeball-juddering, deckhead-hanging, stomach-churning awfulness, at one stage making less than one knot against the storm. But rounded it was, and easier water encountered (though not much, but it seemed like heaven). The song *Mull of Kintyre* was at the top of the charts at the time. It was never again played on board. But the 'Gavvy' was safe and the storm abated. But what of the *Nimrod*? How did she fit into the story?

While we in HMS *Gavinton* fought to survive the storm in the approaches to the Clyde, we could hear *Nimrod's* tragic story unfolding over Channel 16, the emergency VHF radio band. This poor coaster was caught in dangerous waters by a force eleven gale in the North Sea, on the other side of the country. Even as the little 'Hunter' defied the greater storm, the Nimrod's cargo shifted and her doom was sealed. She was too close to the Banks, the shifting sand bars that lie off the eastern shore, for a nearby ship to do anything but watch and report the coaster's forlorn struggle against oblivion.

It took only two hours to change the *Nimrod* from a well-found ship to a declared wreck. It was that quick. That sort of thing can be the 'Banks' speciality'.

These two stories illustrate the fine line that exists between a ship's survival and her demise, when in heavy weather. Seamanship, luck, judgement – and possibly the Book of Psalms – all play their part but the outcome is often in the hands of the Gods. The song is written in the style we equate with a hundred years before. It is only the fifth verse that gives a clue to the actual century concerned.

THE NIMROD

Tune original

It was a wild November, Seventy Seven was the year,
The morning of the fourteenth day, before the light appeared.
The night was black as pitch, m' boys,
the morning was the same.
'Twas then a good ship struck, m' boys,
and Nimrod was her name.

'Twas by the Dudgeon Light,
not far from Dowsing and Smith's Knoll,
That she was struck by wind and wave
that made her list and loll.
The Force Eleven, that she knew was waiting for some prey,
Picked her up and did her down in the twelfth part of a day.

'Oh Save Our Souls!' the Nimrod cried, 'for we are drifting fast.
'The ship is heeling over and we have not long to last.
'We cannot launch the lifeboats
and the Banks are looming large.
'Pray Heaven you can reach us
'ere we fall to Neptune's charge.'

But only one, a coasting ship, was there to see the fate,
Of Nimrod and her gallant crew, but she was there too late,
For Nimrod struck and very soon was lying in her grave.
Her crew threw out the liferafts and were lucky to be saved.

Two hours was all it took to send that ship beneath the waves.
There was not time for Cromer's 'Boat to find a life to save;
But Thirty Two and Thirty Five, so Humber Wireless said,
The helicopters saved the crew
when all thought they were dead.

And we all fear the waters of a Force Eleven Gale,
The clanging of the hatches sound a mournful deathly knell
And we all fear the waters of a Force Eleven Gale,
But we'll live and die as sailormen; m' darlin' fare thee well.

EQULIBRIUM

Though the coasters death,
Scrap-warrant of her melting,
Once mighty, the wave,
Old now and weak, was swamped by,
The launch of a greater Ship.

Anyone who has ever been in fog at sea will know that there is but one word that can do justice to the feeling – *limbo*. Nothing can be seen and, if the sea is calm, there is no reference point to stop you believing that you are floating in a white, empty and intangible world. If you hear a sound you have no way of knowing its direction, for fog plays strange tricks upon the senses. Everything becomes wet and cold. All the mariner can do is proceed with utmost caution, sound the correct signals for his type, size, movement, purpose and direction and hope that every other nearby drifting-soul does likewise.

These days radar, satellite navigation and the like make things easier but they also encourage fools to put their trust in such gadgets and forget the simple rules of seamanship. Picture the Watch Officer on the bridge of a Merchant Coaster, or bigger, surrounded by clever electronic wizardry; warm and dry and sipping a cup of coffee. The doors are closed; the heater is heating and the anti-collision alarm set to ten miles. The ship is making ten knots, the Captain is asleep in his cabin and all is right with the world. Except that outside there is fog. Sure there is nothing on the radar scope that will come within three miles, but there may be something the radar cannot see.

RADAR stands for Radio *Aid* to Direction and Range. AID – as opposed to 'all-seeing magic eye'. No, oh Watchkeeping Officer, put down that coffee cup, don your watch coat, open the doors, post your lookout in the bows, shake the Captain and get out on the bridge wing and listen. Then perhaps you will hear the tinkle of the fisherboat at anchor, away up ahead there.

Fog. This song describes it well. Based on Dickie's haunting tune, which is itself taken from the two notes of the Diaphone foghorn that one can hear along our lighthouse-guarded shores, it gives some insight to the feeling of that limbo experienced in fog at sea. These two notes are so distinctive that they remain in the memory and have instant recognition the moment they are heard.

FOG BOUND

(Bernie Bruen) ~ Tune original (Dickie Barr)

Low-pitched diaphones, grumbling on the air,
Whispering the message for everyone to hear –
Brass-bound fog horns, belching out their call,
Telling of the fog with alarming caterwaul.

The grey wall circles closer in the air,
Cosseting each vessel with individual care
Blind ship, dead ship, whither will you crawl
When its fingers drape your shoulders
with that wet, bone-chilling shawl?

In the mid-Atlantic, imprisoned by despair,
Or blinded in the Channel 'til the Pilot should appear;

The Grand Banks speciality, a flat and oily sea;
The raucous sounding fishing fleet to windward and to lee.

The lighthouse disembodied voice cries, 'Danger! Keep away!'
The restless buoys will toil your path and point the waterway.
Blind ship, dead ship, sounding bell and gong
In the glaring darkness where the ghosting ships belong.

ST VINCENT BY AND BY

Nobly, nobly Cape St Vincent
to the north west died away.
Sunset ran one glorious blood red
reeking, into Cadiz Bay;
Bluish, mid the burning water,
full in face Trafalgar lay;
In the dimmest north east distance,
dawned Gibraltar grand and grey;
'Here and here did England help me.
How can I help England?' say.

Those great lines of Alfred Lord Tennyson still burn with pride and power today but, written as they were in the era of sail, they do not aptly describe the navigation plot of the faster modern warship. As the little minehunter *Gavinton* returned to the Mediterranean, two years after her Gulf of Suez mine clearance adventure, she thought herself in the good company of other, greater ships of the Royal Navy that served England so well in such waters years before. The lines printed here were written there, as *Gavinton* made passage south, past the great Cape and on to Gibraltar.

Slowly, noble Cape St Vincent
to the south east hove in view,
Sunrise fanned, its lurid rays a-seeking,

Ever changing in its hue.
Rocky, proud she stood at noontide,
bearing three one zero true.
Later in the north west distance,
lost from sight, her image flew;
As the ship, that once helped England,
onward steamed to help anew.

3.   Malawi International Airways String Quartet

Malawi International Airways String Quartet (MIASQ) (1974-1976), the number of whose members ranged between five and eight, was a great favourite with the Ship's Company of HMS *Bulwark* and played 78 'concerts' for them during the eighteen months it was in existence. Starting out as the 'Ship's Jug Band Miss Primm and her Shottage Four' (where that name came from is now lost in the mists of time), we changed its name shortly after meeting with two similar bands from HM ships *Fearless* and *Intrepid* in Gibraltar in 1974. These two rival groups went by the imposing names of 'Nelson's Left Arm Band' and 'The Lagos Imperial Steam Tramways Band'. Being the bigger ship, we *had* to have a bigger name. Thus, to complete the trio, MIASQ (pronounced Mee-ass-queue) was born. Known also for a brief but fascinating period when visiting Istanbul as 'The Magnificent Byzantine Minaret Quintet', the ensemble, changing with the whim of the Commodore Naval Drafting, eventually ended up, rather boringly, being officially recognised as the 'New Bulwark Jug Band'. Funny how officialdom takes the edge off things, aint it?

MIASQ played in many and varied places, of which a few were: The Grand Bazaar in Istanbul, the 1975 Malta International Folk Festival (as Top of the Bill), on the postage-stamp-sized flight deck of a Royal Fleet Auxiliary ship in the middle of the Atlantic, at the Governor of Grand Bahamas' Summer Ball and, most notably, in Monaco... On the evening after the

Formula One Grand Prix of 1975, we played in Rosie's Bar, where all the GP mechanics gathered, and later outside the Café de Paris, where the rich and powerful spilled out into Grand Casino Square and joined in the fun. We were eventually invited in to play, but declined the offer, having just an hour or so before been refused entry. We had principles in those days, don't y' know?

Throughout this time the song 'VP Wine' was a firm MIASQ favourite. Written as the 'run-ashore to end all runs-ashore', it should be sung in such a way that one appears to get more and more inebriated as the song progresses. Don't overdo it though, or the last verse will catch you out!

VP WINE

Bruen/Barr Tune: Original

I met her in the Smoking Room of the Rose and Crown,
Black gym-shoes on her feet, one eyelash hanging down;
Her perfume was unusual; it smelt of Clean-O-Pine,
There she offered me that VP wine.

She whispered, 'Hello Sailor'. I answered with a grin.
First she bought me scrumpy and then she bought me gin.
I had three pints of bitter; she had me on the line
When she bought for me that VP wine.

I took a jar of egg-flip and then two tots of rum;
My teeth began to itch and my nose was getting numb
So I had a pint of Pernod which made me feel quite fine
Until she put in front of me that VP wine.

A jug of Southern Comfort and a jar of Irish Mist,
I swallowed what she gave me and developed quite a list.
I fancied Crème de Menthe, she gave me eight or nine
Mixed up in a pot with that VP wine.

I drank a yard of Babycham and Guinness by the quart,
A magnum of tequila, and then I saw she's brought
A gugglet of that effluent, that bastard of the vine,
A foaming flagon of that VP wine.

She gave me port and claret; arrak, mead and grog,
Whiskey, hock, chianti and ten year old egg-nog.
I had hot toddy, porter and a gourd-full of gluvine
And every hour, upon the hour, that VP wine.

I swallowed shots of slivovitz,
Sucked schnapps up through a straw,
Slurped sherry from a samovar, she gave me more and more.
I saw-off stout and saki, mixed with shandy in a stein
But the last thing I remember was that VP wine.

'UNDER THY WINGS WILL I TRUST'

Thus ran the inscription on the crest of HMS *Bulwark*, but whenever a divisional or departmental photograph was taken on the quarterdeck in front of the carving, some Jack-me-Hearty would cover the first letter of the last word with a piece of masking tape just before it was taken. Thus it was always:

'UNDER THY WINGS WILL I RUST'

Hence the great ship was invariably referred to as 'The Rusty "B". And she was rusty, too. It was almost impossible to keep her clear of the stuff for any length of time. Like the painting job on the Forth Bridge, the old one – the famous one – that work went on for ever. Meanwhile to make a commando ship: take an ordinary aircraft carrier, remove all the stores connected with the flying of jets and fixed wing planes and put them some-where else along with the flying machines, convert every available space or compartment into barracks, messdecks, briefing rooms, stores, magazines and the like, fly on a large number of helicopters, their stores, their crews, maintainers, their support, engineers, domestic staff, safety numbers, their observers and pilots, their stewards, cooks, electricians, their armourers ... and all the rest. Embark an entire commando of Royal Marines, with ancillary units and stores. Sail for whichever trouble-spot presently rears its ugly head and, by the time they arrive, everyone will be thoroughly acclimatised, briefed, fit, and prepared for action. What's more, you will have a moveable re-supply and operating base just over the horizon. The two ships that were so converted were HMS *Albion* and HMS *Bulwark*.

Dickie Barr and Bernie Bruen served in both ships in their time and loved them dearly. *Albion* was scrapped in the early '70s but *Bulwark* went on, to be paid off just before the Falklands War started. Would that we had had her there with us – her and the old helicopter cruiser HMS *Blake* – what a difference it would have made. (And how about since then?)

Meanwhile, back to the song. This became the anthem of the ship. To hear it roared from 1,800 throats on an 'Up Channel Night' complete with the band of the Royal Green Jackets, or again, in that final concert of the penultimate 'Last Commission' was to hear the ship's company, the air group and the commando in complete unison with their ship. Wonderful!

Perhaps a few words of explanation here would help your understanding:

Booties were Royal Marines of the embarked force, as opposed to *Cloggies,* who were their Dutch counterparts – and also frequent visitors.

LCP (Short for LCVP) Landing Craft Vehicle and Personnel. Long, open, motorised boxes used by the ships' Royal Marines detachment for taking ashore those of the embarked force who were not lucky enough to go by helicopter (paraffin-pigeon, wokka-wokka, toadfish or chopper).

ASSAULT: Assault Stations: similar to Action Stations except that everyone moves around instead of standing still.

COMPO: Ration packs. Each large box contains ten smaller boxes of food. Each of these has sufficient goodies to keep the serviceman in the field fully operational for 24 hours. There are various menus supplied, ranging from Steak and Kidney Pudding to Chicken Supreme. But each 10-man box contains only one choice from the selection. (This saves the men from fighting among themselves and directs their attention towards the enemy). But if you really want to focus his attention that way, give a Royal Marine menu 'D' and he will immediately vanquish his enemies in order to snaffle their victuals. Well, that's the way the 'Booties' see it. Menu 'D' is of course, corned beef.

ALMA BATTERY: One of the Royal Artillery units assigned to the commando.

MUSTER: Fall in or assemble

THE RUSTY 'B'

(Bruen/Barr) Tune original

Welcome to the Rusty 'B', your life is in our hands.
Come on passage with us to far exotic lands.
We will entertain you and keep you in our care.
Life is really super for the 'Booties'.

Sunday morning, six o'clock, muster in your mess.
How or where you're put ashore is anybody's guess.
Be it helicopter or bouncing L-C-P,
Life is really super for the 'Booties'.

We'll batten down the hatches and close up all the doors;
As you're going to 'Assault', we'll start to take on stores.
You'll have to dodge the beer crates and get there best you can
For life is really super for the 'Booties'.

When you land on 'Red Beach', you'll find you're on your own;
No steaks, no eggs, no fresh bread rolls or tea to wash it down.
You'll find your 'Compo' ration packs are all of letter 'D'
Coz life is really super for the 'Booties'.

Go on Alma Battery, give 'em your support;
If they're lagging at the front then drop a couple short.
As you're Royal Artillery, we'll re-embark you first
For life is really super for the 'Booties'.

So come and join our merry ship and sail the seven seas,
While you're flogging up the hills, we'll sit and take our ease
With cinema and tug-of-war and lots of beer and food galore,
Life is really super for the 'Booties'.

Chorus

So pack your kit, your sleeping bag, your rifle and your mug;
Life is really super for the 'Booties'.

Another MIASQ favourite was the following song, which was written in a dog-watch whilst at sea in the Bay of Biscay. It needed to be sung prior to a run ashore, or, early in a concert, in order to avoid tongue twisting after a few beers.

Most sailors, when away at sea from wives and girlfriends, think lovingly of them, so this song was written with those loved ones in mind. It was one MIASQ song that was listened to intently and not taken up and sung by all, and you can see why!

HYPERCONDRIACOSIS

(Bruen/Barr) ~ Tune original

She has a free-fall shoulder and a dislocated knee,
Her clavicle is critical, her sternum's arthritical,
Her scapular's psychotic and her coccyx is thrombotic,
She's addicted to that osteopathy.

She's pulled her sternumastoids and her gluteus maximi.
Her intercostal triceps have become her quadri-biceps.
Her semitendinosus have destroyed her little toeses.
She's a martyr to that physiotherapy.

She is weedy, she's gone seedy, she's got spas-muscular pain.
Her ulcers are homogenised, her kidneys have been sterilised,
Foreign objects cut from the tangle of her gut,
Radiography is driving her insane.

She lost her contact lenses while syringing out her ears.
She's lost her sense of smell and deodorant as well.
Her tonsils have revolted and her adenoids have bolted
And her larynx and her voice have disappeared.

Her bunions are the biggest that the world has ever seen.
She's got such fallen arches
that she counters counter-marches.
Her corns are astronomical, her toenails anatomical.
She's got verruca's growing on her spleen!

She's had drillings, she's had fillings,
she's had caps upon her teeth.
Her interdental cavities show dietary depravities.
Her supramolar plaque has polyfilled the cracks
And her incisors are rotting underneath.

But she's my darling, she's my beauty,
She's my lady of delight
And I love the bits and pieces
That I gather up each night

This next song sums up MIASQ like nothing else does. It was used to introduce the members to our audiences. We only ever set out to be supremely adequate, entertain the bored and have fun in doing so and that is precisely what we achieved.

THE MIASQ SONG

(Bruen/Barr) ~ Tune original

The Malawi International Airways String Quartet
Has brought the finest sound from the shores of England yet.
A jolly jangling jug band of very high renown
From the rocky shores of Malta to Monte Carlo town.

Chorus:

So pluck it, blow it, strum it or bang it on the ground.
Sing a chorus, clap your hands and join our happy sound.
Stamp your kecks and wave your feet
and shower us in champagne,
With flowers and chocks and kisses, we'll sing it all again.
(and again and again...)

We say that we're a quartet but that's not strictly true.
We're seven fearless mortals standing staunch and true.
Our repertoire is rather large and can be quite amusing
We sing and dance and stand and shout
which can be quite bemusing.

No one listens to Jim Carrick with his banjo-type guitar.
He sits and stuffs his face with a sandwich and cigar.
His glasses perched upon his nose, his tank-top on his chest,
He's like a lost but wise old owl that's fallen from his nest.

We feature Charlie Bullock on his Pogo-stradavarious
His technique is rather splendid and also rather curious
We often turn to him and shout, 'Turn the volume down'
But Charlie's hard of hearing and just returns a frown.

The smallest gadget in our band's the Zither-mandolin.
For such a tiny box it makes by far the greatest din.
Jim Mavin's nimble fingers will caress the guilded frets
But he keeps it rather quiet when he scuppers all our wets

Graham Smith, when time allows,
will play the clarinet
Through the scales he gaily sails
and plays most any set
If it's jazz you like or to your delight'
to hear the rhythm and blues
Then watch him play and swing and sway:
the steps are yours to choose

Our time we take from Brian Wood
who keeps it with his tuba
We nearly lost him once
upon our visit to Aruba
He puffs and blows with all he knows
and wraps it round his neck
By the time we've sung a song or two
he looks a living wreck

Dickie Barr's our leader
and he strums a mean guitar.
Without him we'd be knackered
coz we need his motor car.
His voice is soft and sexy.
He can yoddle, he can croon
But we wish he'd take his guitar
and weld it into tune.

And so to that creation
by the name of Bernie Bruen
Who's knee high kicks and ankle flicks
will surely be his ruin
The songs he writes will hit the heights,
and keep us all a-going

With his giant gazoo, duck calls too,
and his swanee whistle blowing

It's such a pity that the songs we sing
ain't heard by thousands more
The Pixie, Gnome, Happy Hippy and Johnny Bugger-all
VP Wine, The Rusty B, The Scrumpy Vat, no jest
Are the songs that all the BULWARKS love to sing the best

At the time of its writing in 1975, the following was a topical song. Looking at it now, we doubt that many would recall the issues of the day or the main characters. Bernie and Richard wrote it during a 'Stand Easy' (20 minutes tea break) whilst in HMS *Bulwark*. However, from a purely historic point, it is probably worthy of inclusion:

INTERNATIONAL PROTESTORS

(Bruen/Barr) ~ Tune original

We are the International Protesters
we demonstrate all day in almost every way
We wear way out clothes and long, long hair
We march sit or lie down anywhere
We are International Protesters, yeah
We are International Protesters.
Hold your placards in the air,
let the people stop and stare
We shall not be moved.

We protest for... (pause)

Teachers' pay, Antony Gray,
Enoch Powell, Dennis Howell,
Georgie Best, Rudolph Hess,
Rin Tin Tin, Ho Chi Minn,
Farmers' prices, shipyard strikers

and we'll sing the marchers' song,
Ban the Bomb!

We protest against... (pause)

Too much road tax, Labour's wise-cracks,
teeny-boppers, London coppers,
The Springbok tour, the Vietnam war,
National Health and Royalty's wealth,
Israeli jets and levied bets
and we'll sing the marchers' song,
Ban the Bomb!

We protest at...

Birmingham, Twickenham,
Bangkok and Holy Lough (loch),
Northern Ireland, down in Thailand,
Mexico, Tokyo, Grosvenor Square or anywhere
and we'll sing the marchers' song...
BAN THE BOMB!

This next song was by far, the most requested song MIASQ ever had. The only place where an audience had trouble following it was in the Grand Bazaar in Istanbul, so no surprises there. Also, during the time that we spent in Cabaret after leaving *Bulwark*, it became a favourite with audiences whenever and wherever we played. This is the song, the chorus of which, provided a platform for Bernie's amazing high kicks and pirouettes.

THE PIXIE SONG

(Bruen) ~ Tune original

On Abberly Bank, back of Clows Top and Cleobury,
Not far from the Washing Pool and the Old Martley Road

And hard by the Dark Wood, where rooks keep their watches,
There's a small bramble bush – the abode of a toad.

Chorus:

Aarrh, aarrh, I'm a little pixie.
Aarrh, aarrh, I skip around all day.
Aarrh, aarrh, some parsnip wine'll fix 'ee.
It makes me young and frisky when the fairies are at play.

Now, this toad had a visa stamped into his passport,
A six months work-permit to help pay his way;
An immigrant visitor, that was his station,
A Horned Toad who hailed from the U S of A.

Aloysius deVerre Debonaire was his 'handle'.
His skin was as slimy and horny as that.
He lived all alone in his bramble-bush shelter
And beat-up the fairies with a small cricket bat.

Now, the fairy policeman got fed-up and chocker
And, as for the young fairy Doctor, he found
That the mending of gossamer wings and smashed noses
Was more than his magical powers could confound.

So, a letter they wrote on a frost-spangled dew-drop
And sent it by bluebird away 'cross the sea;
And they got for themselves a hired toad from Texas
Who shot Aloysius for a magical fee.

So, if you're a toad and you live in the brambles
And you beat fairies up at least six times a day,
Then beware of the toad in the tall hat from Texas.
He's been granted asylum and the fairies are gay!

Another MIASQ favourite and oft requested by the crew of
Bulwark, this song was composed by Bernie, who was a dab
hand at rally driving. It received rapturous applause in Rosies

Bar, Monte Carlo, from crews of the major Formula 1 teams on evening of the 1975 Monaco Grand Prix.

THE AUTOMOTIVE ALCOHOLIC ROADHOG

(Bernie Bruen)

Now, you've heard them all before in every Pub and Bar,
The man who seems to worship the religion of the car.
He'll tell you of the journeys that he's made both far and wide,
The roads he used to get there.
He will number them with pride:
The 'A eleven', 'B thirteen' and roadworks outside Rhyll
And how he averaged thirty and you guess he always will;

But I'm the Automotive Alcoholic Roadhog,
I've got a car that really beats them all.
I've had the chassis lowered 'til it sits upon the ground,
Got 'meggas' up my tail pipe to amplify the sound.
In the middle of the night, I'll drive round and round the town.
I'm the Automotive Alcoholic Roadhog.

Well, you've heard them all before in every Pub and Bar,
The man who seems to worship the religion of the car.
You've seen him with his chequered hat
and handlebar moustache,
Who says he's driven thirty years "...and never had a craash!"
And, when you see his car, you're not surprised he's still alive
For he'll polish it each Sunday and it never leaves his drive;

But I'm the Automotive Alcoholic Roadhog,
I've got a car that really beats them all.
I've got so many spotlights that my car looks like a toad.
At night, when you are driving, though my circuits overload,
I'll flash the whole lot at you 'til you drive right off the road.
I'm the Automotive Alcoholic Roadhog.

Yes, you've heard them all before in every Pub and Bar,
The man who seems to worship the religion of the car.

You've seen the one whose window-stickers
prove he's travelled far,
Who hugs the middle of the road at twenty miles an hour.
You never can get past him,
though you hoot and flash and wave.
His car and he have got one foot and one wheel in the grave;

But I'm the Automotive Alcoholic Roadhog,
I've got a car that really beats them all.
My 'slipstream-double-torque-converter-aerofoil' is new,
I find, in heavy traffic, when I'm stuck behind that queue
That the faster that I drive
the smaller gaps I can get through.
I'm the Automotive Alcoholic Roadhog.

Here are two more MIASQ favourites, oft requested both at concerts onboard and when ashore and both sung at both the 1973 and 1975 International Folk Festivals of Malta.

HAPPY HIPPY

(Barr) Tune original

I want to be a happy little hippy
with bells hanging down and a flower in my hair.
I want to be a happy little hippy
but I'm in the Navy and it just ain't fair

I want to go to sunny California,
see all those hippies and be a hippy too
I want to go to a love-in every Sunday,
want to be a hippy – how about you?

I want to play in a psychedelic pop group
I want to smash my guitar across my knee
I want to play to those lovely flower people
but I'm fragile and guitars ain't free.

I want to be a happy little hippy
with bells hanging down and a flower in my ear
I want to be a happy little hippy
but I'm on my ship and I can't get near

I want to smoke marijuana
under orange trees,
I want smoke marijuana till I'm high
I want to ride on an old Lambretta
and wear a multi-coloured flowered tie

I want to be a happy little hippy
with bells hanging down and a flower in my hair
I want to be a happy little hippy
but I'm in the Navy and it just ain't fair

PUFF THE ROCKER DRAGON

(Dickie Barr) ~ Tune: Puff The Magic Dragon

Puff the Rocker Dragon lived at Clacton by the sea
And he frolicked along the promenade on his twin 500cc
All the other dragons they loved the Rocker Puff
And they bought him studded belts and chains
and other rocker stuff.

He travelled far and wide, in England and in Wales
Girls in leathers fell for him and listened to his tales
He told them of his exploits and made them laugh aloud
He was to them a 'regular swell' of him they were so proud.

But! One night while three abreast on the M4 to Bridgend
He lost control, began to roll and missed a left hand bend
He hurtled through a hedgerow,
came to rest in long green graaass
With his rear wheel wrapped around his neck
and his handlebars up his... nose!

4.   DIVING

Probably the best way to introduce this chapter is with the song 'THE DIVERS LOT'. The year that it was composed is given away by the last verse – that momentous year of the Man on the Moon. It was composed by one of a group of Dartmouth Caydets who were attending a three week Ships Divers Course. Diving courses by nature were, and still are, extremely tough and the failure rate was about 75% in those days. To have a 100% pass was unheard of. But when the trainees are all of one mind, work hard together, play hard together and put their all into the job, then it becomes enjoyable and great things are achieved, like a 100% pass! This song gives a glimpse of the spirit that can be achieved. It has survived for over forty years and is just as applicable today as it was then, to any diver, anywhere.

THE DIVERS' LOT

Tune: A Policemen's Lot Is Not A Happy One

I'm a diver. I'm for diving and my buddy
Gives me the helping hand that I require.
For, when I'm down the bottom where it's muddy,
He'll haul me up, in case I should expire.
And later we'll go down unto the Ale House
To find out how much beer we can consume.
Yes, together we'll go to the beer-retail-house
And we'll stay there all the sunny afternoon.

Now, the Boss has got himself a little notebook
And in it he writes down the time we spends

With our breathing-sets beneath the rippling waters
And who is who, and who that 'who' attends.
He enters all the info on the pages
And we don't worry, coz we know that soon
He will look and see we've been down there for ages
And haul us up before the afternoon.

Sometimes you'll find a girlfriend, wife or mother
Will come out in our boat to see us dive;
And she'll marvel at our care for one another
As we make sure that we all remain alive.
But she may think there's trouble or there's danger,
As for astronauts who walk upon the moon,
So we'll take her down the pub and there we'll range her
Coz we'll stay there all the sunny afternoon.

Chorus:

Yes, we'll all go down unto the nearby Ale House
And we'll stay there all the sunny afternoon.

This next song is a Parody on a Parody – that immortal poem 'You are Old, Father William' – this features My Old Mate, Uncle Joe, as the subject. The tune that accompanies the piece was written for him some years before and has been successfully combined with the words to produce an enjoyable, if somewhat difficult-to-sing, song. They are both offered out of sincerest regard and affection. Father Joe Maher is an elderly Chief Diver chatting idly with a young 'sprog' sailor during the Dog Watches at sea.

FATHER MAHER

Tune: Original 'Me ol' Mate'

'You are old, Father Maher,' the new sailor said,
'And your eyebrows and whiskers below 'em
Are tangled and matted and black as old tar,
Pray, how did you manage to grow 'em?'

'In my youth,' said the Chief, as he growled through his set,
'My chin was quite downy, you know,
'But I rubbed it twice daily with tallow and grease,
'Boot-topping, shale-oil and dough.'

'You are old, Father Maher,' the new sailor said,
'Your skin is like parchment and leather;
'Your brow is so wrinkled and knuckles so gnarled,
'Is it all from the wind and the weather?'

'You impertinent upstart!' the old Chief retorted,
'When young, my complexion was pale
'But I've had a few women and tattooed my chest
'And drunk a few barrels of ale.'

'You are old, Father Maher,' the new sailor said,
'Yet your seamanship leaves me amazed
'For you knot and you splice in the wink of an eye
'And your boat-handling's famous and praised.'

'How observant you are,' the Ancient replied,
'For my thumbs were like fids when a lad,
'My fingers were spikes and my teeth held the sheets
'Of the sails when the weather got bad.'

'You are old, Father Maher,' the new sailor said,
'And you spin your wisdom and charms
'When you sit on the bollard, a-whiling the Dogs
'Enthralling us all with your yarns.'

'You're a kindly young lad,' the old Chief rejoined,
But don't believe all that I tell 'ee;

'For I gained all my wisdom while out on patrol,
In Simonstown, 'Singers' and Delhi'.

'You are old, Father Maher. I've said it before,
'Though you'll sign-on again, there's no doubt.
'Don't you think that it's time you retired from the sea
'To go fishing for mackerel and trout?'

'What incredible cheek!' roared the Chief in a rage.
'A curse on you new-navy 'sprogs'!
'You've wasted my time – so get Bluebell (Brasso) and Rags
'And you'll work right the way through the Dogs!'

Up in the backwaters of Portsmouth Harbour lies Horsea Island; now, with road development, no longer an island at all. Horsea was built to house a torpedo testing range and, as it contained a long, thin, straight, deepish stretch of brackish water, soon became the 'home' of the Clearance Diving Branch. This was where divers spent many hours and days undergoing their training and much loved it is by all of them. Since the reclamation of the surrounding areas for building, road development and the like, the extensive mud flats that surround the place have disappeared and those which are left have changed a great deal. Mud running is a bit of a misnomer really for you could hardly run in the normal sense of the word. What you actually did, if you were good, was to imitate the cross-country skier, or if you were not, the beached whale. The Mud-Run was the finest form of exercise to get a diver fit for his job and some of us actually did it for fun too. A group of officer cadets (yes, those mentioned earlier) from Dartmouth arrived at Horsea in the summer leave of 1969 and after three weeks qualified as Ships Diving Officers, with a one hundred per cent pass.

Over the next few years, some of that happy bunch progressed to the ultimate position of Clearance Divers (CDs). The Horsea Island or Mud-Run Song was one that Bernie wrote for that first course. As he stated later. "In those days we were fit enough and good enough to sing it as we ran"

THE MUD-RUN SONG

(Bruen) Tune: 'Mud, Glorious Mud'

All Diving Officers invariably find
That a mud-run is good for the soul.
CD Petty Officers instil in their mind
It will help reach their ultimate goal.
They sweat and they swear and their temperatures rise
As they struggle through treacle-like slime;
For weak and for strong, they all know this song
And sing it most of the time.

Mud, mud, black Horsea mud;
Nothing quite like it for heating the blood.
So come from the dry land down to the Island
And there let us try our 'and at Horseaous mud.

Soft, black and sticky, it comes up to your knees
And occasionally up to your waist.
If you taste an icky-bit, don't swallow it, please,
For it has a peculiar taste.
Don't stop or you'll sink. Don't sit or slow down.
Keep moving, whatever the pain;
Or else, have no doubt, you'll soon hear the shout
Of the Chief calling, 'Go round again!'

Mud, mud, black Horsea mud.
Nothing quite like it for heating the blood.
So come from the dry land, down to the Island
And there let us try our 'and at Horseaous mud.

Based on a popular rugby song of the day, this is another survivor from that 1969 Ship's Diving Officer Course. It is great for the pub or travelling in the coach and lends itself to lots of noise and stamping of feet. Don't worry if you do not understand the words, any Clearance Diver will be happy to explain.

CLEARANCE DIVERS' SONG

Bernie Bruen Tune: The Ash Grove

When we started diving,
We were told that conniving
Was certainly thriving
Among the CDs.

A brass one and a copper one,
A smalley one and a whoppa one,
A Momma one and a Poppa one
They filched from the seas

And the air from his suit-inflation,
The air from his suit-inflation,
The air from his suit-inflation
Went up to his knees.

A copper one and a brass one
And a sticky-ickie on the last one,
And the air from his suit-inflation
Went up to his knees.

The old, handraulic diver's air-pump, that wooden, box-like contraption with two 'gurt' big handle-wheels on the side, had to be wound and wound, just as steady as could be, to provide a supply of air to the diver down below. In his suit and weights, boots and harness, he was scarcely able to move on deck. The diver wore a red woollen cap that kept him warm beneath the waves but also marked him as the immobile man above. Derrick operators and later, crane drivers could easily see just where he was and keep their loads clear of him. Once the diver was equipped with all his gear – his warm woollens, weights, short-sword (the traditional diver's knife), yoke and helmet, and had been lowered to the bottom, he was free. In his own submerged world the diver could move with relative ease, albeit somewhat slowly, and there was no-one there to get in the way. The standard 'hard hat' divers' were a special breed of men who were not averse to a drop o' rum on completion of the day's work either. I expect that there were Pumpman's Chanties but I have never heard of one yet. Until I do, this one's fine for me. *(The succeeding verses follow the same format as the first verse)*

DIVER DOWN BELOW

A Pumpman's Shanty Tune original

Shantyman: Put your woollen jumpers on.

All: Diver down below.

Shantyman: Put your woollen jumpers on

All: Diver down below. Away down diver – Down diver, down.

Shantyman: Put your woollen jumpers on.

All: Diver down below

Shantyman: Put your suit of canvas on.

All: (Repeat, as for 'All' above)

Shantyman: Put your belt and short sword on.

Shantyman: Buckle up your weighted boots.

Shantyman: Put your yoke and helmet on.

Shantyman: Strap your weights and lifeline on.

Shantyman: Wind the handles of the pump.

Shantyman: Send him down his breathing air.

Shantyman: Haul him up his time is done.

Shantyman: Pour the man his tot of rum.

Shantyman: Put your woollen jumpers on.

There is an eternal war that is fought between the wind, waves and flowing water on the one hand and the land on the other. In the end there can be but one victor and one vanquished: the sea must win and the land disappear for ever. This conflict has been joined since the dawn of time and will continue until that ultimate day when the last rock finally disappears beneath the low-water mark. But there is a third party; one spawned as a creature of the sea. This crawling thing forsook its mother element to find a drier, steadier life ashore. After millions of years it evolved into Man, who in his season, puny though his efforts were, sought to protect the land from the erosion that ate away its edges. Through the ages, with growing confidence, Man triumphed for a time, but saw his efforts swept away and so redoubled his endeavours. Yet in Man's primeval senses, something must have stirred, to call him back to that terrible mother he once knew. First floating upon the waters, and later, back below the waves where life commenced.

Has man now come full circle? Has he at last forsaken his overcrowded, land-based home? These must be the questions that the timeless sea-thoughts asked, when they first saw a diver with his mask, fins and spear-gun.

THE DIVER

A verse

Green turns to green and black to black.
Nocturnal creatures stretch and listen to the news.
Grand Masters of their private world,
The age-old fossils of an unknown sea
Step back and wait their turn to die.

The noise of silence sheds a blindfold ear
In vain attempt to capture sounds unheard.
The sea itself forbears to move
With such a fervour it has known
And stops a-while to follow novel movement.

The only part that knows this new intrusion
Is far above, dispersed by foam and wind.
It cannot pass the message to the depths
That here arrives a kindred of them all;
But waits to hear the judgement of the deep.

They circle round to watch from far
And feel with fingers lighter than the air above.
They ask each other, what can be
This compromise of such as they, unseen before
Yet somehow in their spirit hated for betrayal.

And so they wait to see if all is well
And watch this goggle eye,
Itself positioned like an omen.
Has it come to stay or leave?
Is it of a friendly nature
Or, at war with creatures of their sort?

They watch and feel an apprehensive calm,
Not knowing if it be The One,
Long lost and hoped for to return.
A flash, a pressure and a noise;
A shaft of light that skims with lightning speed
And one, a brother, lives no more.

As from the depths this alien ascends,
They know, in truth and death,
This is the ally of the land,
Their age-old foe.

5.   Mines & Minehunting

Minesweeping and Minehunting are two of the least glamorous roles that the Royal Navy are tasked with performing, yet, they are vitally important to the safety of the fleet, merchantmen and, as two world wars are testament to, the safety of the nation. In 1970, the Royal Navy had over 70 ships on station all around the world dealing with the disposal of, or making safe, these explosive devices. Often considered the most dangerous of tasks, there were more than 5000 sailors involved in this unsung branch of the Navy and, the ships in which they sailed were small, cramped and most uncomfortable to be in, in anything over a moderate gale. This chapter then, is dedicated to those men of the Mine Warfare branch of the Royal Navy, who worked the 'Tons' and before them, the 'Algerines' in what was known as 'the Dangerous Game'.

This next song is based on that written for and about Leading Seaman (MW) Barry Batten, the Buffer of HMS Gavinton, by Chief Electrical Artificer Laurie Young, when we all served onboard together in the late seventies. A few words of explanation about this Minesweeping song may make it a little easier to understand and perhaps give a small insight into that particular 'black art'.

The Forth. Much of the practice sweeping carried out by the Royal Navy is done in the Firth of Forth.

The Bridges: The two constructions that span that waterway. The rail bridge is old and very famous. The road bridge is not.

'Sweeping' Hats: Sported by Sweepdeck Crews to keep the head warm and show a certain individual style, they range from

the standard knitted cap to the bowler hat. The First Lieutenant in this song had a particularly fine rabbit-skin in affair.

Stream the Gear: The process of hoisting all that complicated collection of wires, floats and other paraphernalia over the stern and deploying it in an orderly manner.

Bos'n in his Chair: In order to control the streaming operation, the Petty Officer Seaman in charge would perch himself in a specially constructed seat that was the aftermost structure in the ship. Poised above the waves, between the two outwards-rushing sweepwires, he would communicate his wishes by sign language. This was quicker than the more usual method of shouting, easier on the ear and reserved the vocal medium for emergencies.

The Winch: Rather prone to burning out 'paxoline blocks' (No, I don't know what they are either but that's what the technocrats told us), the winch which controlled the sweep-wires and other associated gear, normally broke down just as one believed that everything was going perfectly.

Cropper and Axe: Emergency equipment kept ready to hand, so that in dire emergency when 'kites' went flying and life was threatened by rogue gear, the whole lot could be cut away and left to sink astern. Fortunately this very seldom happened.

Kite: A large, metal venetian-blind affair used to drag the wires down to their operating depth below the ship. Sometimes, when the gear was being recovered, it would take off into the air and go 'flying'. This was when a good Sweepdeck Director, backed up by an experienced crew, would really come into his own; for a 'flying' kite was not only extremely hazardous but could completely ruin your itinerary, the gear and the Captain's day.

Cutters: 'V'-shaped blades set at intervals upon the 'wire' to cut the mooring cables of mines being swept. More effective, however, was the variety that incorporated an explosively triggered chisel and anvil to perform the same task.

Sonar: The alternative and more modern method of mine clearance. Rather than steaming along dragging one's equipment behind, it is much safer to proceed cautiously, looking ahead and round about searching for mines with a sonar beam. This method was used very effectively in the Gulf of Suez clearance in 1984 and is called mine hunting.

Hook: The Killick Anchor displayed on the arm, or these days on the shoulder straps, to denote the rating of a Leading Seaman. Hence his nickname of 'Hookey'.

The Old Tin Gear: The minesweeping man's generic term for the collection of floats, kites, otters, cutters, noise-makers, grips and wires that make up a 'sweep'.

THE OLD TIN GEAR

Laurie Young

We're sailing down the Forth, me lads,
The Bridges lie astern,
The Jimmy's donned his 'sweeping' hat,
We'll stream the gear again.

The Bos'n's in his favourite chair,
The morning's sweep is planned,
He indicates the orders,
With the gestures of his hand.

The driver of the winch is there,
With nothing much to say.
He's praying hard the winch will last,
Until the close of play.

The Crew are on the sweeping deck,
Lifejackets on their backs;
There's wire and poles and tins of grease,
A cropper and an axe.

The sweep is out. The 'kite' is down,
The cutters are all set.
The tea is made. 'Come quickly, lads,
We've just time for a wet.'

There's Paddy, Taff and Nobby there,
Young 'Arry's 'elping too,
In all Rosyth you'll never find,
A better sweepdeck crew.

The wire is in. The gear is stowed,
The course we set is west,
But for finding mines it must be said,
That Sonar is the best!

Chorus

For now I've got my 'hook' up,
There is nothing that I fear.
I'm the Gaffer of the lads,
Who stream the Old Tin Gear.

Back in 1970 and beyond, there were many 'TON' Class Mine-sweepers and Minehunters, belonging to the Royal Navy, operating around the world. Before the days of personal stereos, video machines and worldwide television, sailors made their own entertainment. This song was a kind of game that the crews used to play of an evening. The idea was simply to try and remember the words. This version dates from my days in Bahrain with the 9th Mine Countermeasures Squadron. There are probably other versions but who remembers them, or indeed sings them now?

Today, the 'Tons' have all being replaced by much more expensive vessels. This is therefore a look into the past and a celebration of those wonderful little wooden ships, the workhorses of that larger, more widespread Royal Navy of not-so-long-ago.

Bernie Bruen

Notes:

1) 'Drunkerton' was the nickname given to HMS *Soberton*.
2) HMS *Grafton* was actually a Type 14 Frigate but always thought to be a Minesweeper because of the 'ton' on the end of its name.

THE TON'S TEA PARTY

Tune: Traditional

Tarlton, Alcaston, Aldington, Alverton,
Appleton, Alfriston and Bronington's crew;
Blaxton, Bevington, Bildeston, Brereton,
Bossington, Bickington and Brinton came too.

Beachampton, Chediston, Durweston, Darlaston,
Dilston, Dumbleton and Dunkerton's crew;
Chilton, Derriton, Essington, Maddiston,
Gavinton, Glasserton and Crofton came too.

Hexton, Hickleton, Hazleton, Hubberston,
Crichton, Highburton and Hodgeston's crew;
Ilmington, Iveston, Kedleston, Kellington,
Kirkliston, Lullington came along too.

Laleston, Lewiston, Nurton and Overton,
Maxton, Pollington and Puncheston's crew;-
Oulston, Oakington, Packington, Rennington,
Monkton, Castleton and Repton came too.

Santon, Singleton, Sheraton, Shavington,
Stratton, Stubbington and Thankerton's crew;
Soberton, Drunkerton, Wennington, Walkerton,
Whitton, Wasperton and Wiston came too.

Wilton, Wolverton, Wotton and Woolaston,
Brought Cuxton, Upton and Yarnton there too.
Grafton was the only one, the only one not a Ton
But they let her come for the fun and she arrived too.

Ashton, Belton, Boulston, Chilton,
Dufton, Shoulton and Fittleton were
unable to make it as they were patrolling on
Fishery Protection duties at the time.

1984 saw five small ships of the Royal Navy as part of an international effort to clear the Gulf of Suez and Red Sea of mines that had already disabled several merchant vessels. Hunting for mines, which, is different from 'Mine Sweeping', is a tricky business, and this was the first time the Royal Navy had ever done it 'for real'. By the end of the three months that it took to clear their sector, many strange and peculiar items had been found on the sea bed by these little ships; they ranged from a complete motor boat to the proverbial kitchen sink. One ship, however, found what everyone had been seeking – and more. Not only did they uncover one of the rogue mines (the only one to be found, as it turned out) but also disposed of a World War Two German magnetic mine that, even after forty years beneath the waves, detonated with a spectacularly satisfying explosion. The rogue mine itself was duly taken apart by a team of divers, the leader of whom, Terry Settle, was awarded the Queen's Gallantry Medal for his bravery and expertise in defusing the weapon. So, mission completed, the five little ships returned home, past Port Said (on the port side), through the Med and back to the UK. Three months of tension and risk had produced a few more grey hairs but the spirit of the crews was never daunted. This little nonsense verse portrays how, in all such situations, the spark of humour always wins through. That's what makes us Brits special.

THE MINE

'I've found a mine!' the cry was heard.
'It's big and black and sort of round.'
But, answer came there – not a word,
A studied, silent lack of sound.

'Look! See those bits all sticking out,
'There's lots of wire and levers there,
'A square, black box-thing. There's no doubt
'A great, big, ugly mine. D'you hear?'

But one by one they turned away,
And disappeared, each down his hole,
'We want to sink those Ships of Grey,'
'Not go dig for chuffin' coal!'

Every now and then, a particular and individual ship will appear in the ascendancy and, through a strange chemistry concerning time, place and crew, shine out like the Morning Star at Nautical Twilight. HMS *Gavinton* ('Gavvy' for those who knew her) was such a ship. In the latter half of the seventies, under her Captain, Lieutenant Commander Robbie Kerr, Royal Navy, she rose to a level of excellence that surpassed all other 'Tons' and made her an example for other ships of the Fleet. 'Robbie' was followed in Command by the redoubtable Bob Pilling, a famed clearance diver of his day, who took Gavvy even higher up the ladder of success. Five years later she appeared again in that position of excellence and became the only Minehunter to carry out successfully her designed role under 'real' conditions, and finding a previously unknown mine in the process. From that time, until she finally paid-off after thirty-two years continual front-line service, Gavvy remained at the very top.

But what was so special about those last two years was that, without anyone seeming to try, Gavvy was that most elusive of creatures – a happy ship. People in high places seemed most concerned when, month after month, the punishment return showed...'NIL'...Something must be wrong,' they said. 'This must be investigated,' they decided. Poor Gavvy had more visits from the 'faerie folk' of the Navy than you could shake a wicked stick at. Strange people from the nether world of Environmental Husbandry Research, Electronic Restriction Control and even Navigation Surfaces Refurbishment, all paid visits, did their stuff, drank the Wardroom's gin and departed. They found nothing. There was nothing to find. *Gavinton* was simply happy. There was a saying at the time:

'It's great to be a Gavvy.'

Does this sound strange to you? An explanation. Anyone who is part of a Ship's Company becomes part of the ship. So the crew of *Gavinton* were 'Gavintons' and any individual was 'A Gavinton', or a 'Gavvy' for short. Gavintons' enjoyed life; had a sense of fun; would pick wild flowers for their First Lieutenant when he was on duty and could not go to the picnic. Gavintons' ran the London Marathon; juggled onions at the fo'c'sle-head when entering harbour; ran congas round the upper deck and treasure hunts in Edinburgh. Gavintons' skii'd, tobogganed and cycled. But, above all worked, achieved and set the records straight – and those records, that still stand for 'Tons' to this day, were their records. So, with great pride in their little ship, the Gavvys had this song to sing.

GAVVY

Tune: Maggie Mae

When it comes to finding mines,
Running down the dotted lines,
Using Hifix, Decca or a Dan,
You could name 'most any Ton
But you'll still come back to one
Who says, when others say they can't, 'We can!'

If you want to stay on task
Then you've only got to ask
The Gavinton to show you how it's done.
She's been there the longest yet;
As a record I will bet,
She will stay renowned the longest on-task Ton.

She's the Queen of all the 'V's.
She's the tops, she's bound to please.
She's the very best there is, it's true to say.
Even Royalty has noted,
In whose company she's floated,
That she's always there but never in the way.

Whether boarding other ships,
Making mine-disposal dips
Or finding brand-new, undiscovered mines,
She will challenge all she's met,
To beat the records that she's set,
Or else to sing with her the next few/lines.

Oh, the word is surely out,
And there isn't any doubt,
No matter where the mines and short-scopes lay,
For all the other crews,

Have surely heard the news,
And they all admit that 'Gavvy' rules, OK!'

BRINTON BACKBREAKER COCKTAIL

This was invented aboard HMS *Brinton*, when part of the 9th MCM Squadron in 1970. There were two bottles of Cinzano Bianco in the bar that nobody ever drank and the First Lieutenant and midshipman were invited to invent a suitably popular cocktail that would use up the stocks. The intrepid pair did eventually discover the solution (below) but in the process consumed all the Cinzano. It was some time later, after much wheeling and dealing, that a further supply of the particular beverage was obtained and the rest of the Squadron was able to sample the concoction.

Its debut was to coincide with the Persian Gulf Premier of the film 'True Grit', which was to be shown on board. Unfortunately there were problems with the electrical supply, not only in HMS *Brinton* but in the adjacent ships, so the film was never shown in its entirety. Every time it was started, 'bang' went another fuse, a generator tripped or the cable started smoking and the lamp blew. In consequence, the assembled guests watched the opening credits five times in all and consumed several trays of the 'Backbreakers'. This cocktail became most popular, particularly with the ladies. So here's what you do:

Take a tall glass, fill it with ice and rattle it round a little. Insert five drops of Angostura Bitters and a meaningful tot of Plymouth Gin. Add to this an ordinary measure of Cinzano Bianco and top up with Ginger Ale. Garnish with little bits of lemon, a cherry and the leaf of a mint plant, if you must, but really you would be better off just drinking the concoction while you thought about it...

Years later another potion was blended by the same Midshipman, who was now a two-and-a-half (Lieutenant Commander) and who had, in the meantime, been the Gavinton's First Lieutenant. Now, appointed in command of HMS *Brinton*, it appeared that the wheel would turn a full circle and the Midshipman would take his recipe back to the Gulf. (It was 1984 and the Red Sea had been mined – the Dhow Squadron was reborn.) But this was not to be, exactly, for at the last minute the erstwhile returnee was given a 'pier-head jump' to take command of his old friend the 'Gavvy'. Brinton accompanied 'Gavvy' to the Gulf of Suez and the recipe for the Backbreaker was passed to 'Brinton's Captain. The 'Gavinton Milkshake' or 'Gimme a Gavvy!' (below) was invented in celebration of the success of the clearance operation and of everyone's survival. Here's how you make it:

Carefully take a brandy glass half full of crushed ice. Pour in a measure of Baileys. Quickly add a tot of good Rum and another of Drambuie. Stir it all round with your index finger. Sit back, put your feet up and relax...

Oh! And don't forget to drink it!

M1114 – HMS BRINTON

Here is the same midshipman, who is a month or two into his first appointment in one of Her Majesty's ships and whose day has not been going too well. In fact, now that his initial 'first ship' excitement has worn off and the hard work of these minesweepers has him in its grip, the realities of life press heavily upon him. Several things have happened in the last few weeks to put the midshipman in a pensive frame of mind. His Bofors Gun refused to fire when on the range the other day and the Captain was, not unnaturally, a little short tempered about the affair.

The First Lieutenant with whom he shares a cabin insists that anyone looking in to the compartment at any time of the day or night should be convinced that no one actually lives in it. This seems to be taking neatness too far and has strained their relationship somewhat. Furthermore, he has been making some silly mistakes on the bridge recently and, although still under training, feels that he has let his Captain down. Not being the brightest of people, in fact a bit of a plodder, the midshipman is not absorbing knowledge as fast as he should.

And then there was the case of the passing Senior Officer to whom he missed paying marks of respect when 'Duty Cutie'. A stupid mistake but easily done. Hence his presence on board when everyone else is ashore. He is under stoppage of leave. So he is not feeling too happy as he sits in the empty Wardroom, listening to the sounds of the ship, feeling her movement and sensing the ghosts of past minesweepers:

> *I sit, I stare, I look, I see;*
> *The music softly steals away,*
> *And overflows all other sounds;*
> *Smoothes the world in which I live,*
> *And forms a balm to ease the mind.*
>
> *I sit, I stare, I look, I see;*
> *A hum of metal fills the air*
> *And covers up all spaces void;*
> *Smoothes the world in which I live*
> *And forms a balm to ease the mind.*

Were I to take six paces back from where I sit,
I think my heart would die within my eyes;
The change is great and greater yet, outside.

I stand, I stare, I look, I see;
A beauty made by men with minds of steel,
A sound to reach the pitying ear
And maybe set the soul a-fire.
A colour all as one and never dead,
A colour live to all experience.

I stand, I hear, I sense, I feel
A world of violence, yet unborn;
A small and frail, forgotten craft
Waiting like her sisters,
Ships of Ostend and Zeebrugge

HMS GAVINTON D.E.D SONG

Tune: 'Dream' by the Everly Brothers

The Gavinton has broken own.
The petrol's gone, see the 'Jimmy' frown
But if we were to go on like this
We'd drow-ow-ow-own, we'd all drown.

The sonar will not train;
The deck lets in the rain,
Any time, night or day.
The only trouble is, gee-wizz,
The garden-wall's fallen away.
The winch don't, work; the WEO's tried
The lights are duff, it's dark inside
And all we ever wanted was a BMP'
And a D.E.D Ah ha.

Port engine will not go
Coz the/lube-oil will not flow;

Steering gear's shot away.
The generators fail. Make sail!
It wasn't like this in the Bay.
The wardroom heads
Try to explode.
The switchboard's wet,
Won't take the load
But all we ever wanted was BMP,
And a D.E.D.

The Brinton's in the Clyde,
Being pushed round by the tide,
Coz only one engine works.
She's gonna have to make do
While we snaffle all of her perks.

The dockyard has – given us this gift,
They're putting us on the synchrolift
And now we find that we have got
A, D.E.D. – early, An early D.E.D.[1]

Gavinton returned to Rosyth for repairs after an horrific encounter with a force 12 storm in the North Sea during which parts of her supersructure were swept away and there was flooding below. Losing all power due to a fire in the generator, the ship was blind and helpless so had to heave-to until morning before limping homewards. The crew, with the humour that surfaces at such times, penned this ode and sang it to the tune of the Everly Brothers song 'Dream.'

Does it niggle you when someone spells your name wrong? From the highest to the lowest, people seem to have continually

---

[1] Note: D.E.D is a 'Docking and Essential Defect' repair scenario.

spelled 'Gavvy's' name with an extra 'G'. It did little good to write polite letters pointing out that there was only one 'G' in the handle, no one seemed to take any notice. Yes, it began to niggle. The solution seemed to be to send 'the world' a signal to the effect that we did not require that second 'G', thank you!

GAVINTON'S 'G'

Gavinton's with one 'G',
Anything else is OTT.
Very concerned are we
In this matter of policy.
Not to spell it correctly
Gives us feelings of severe frustration.
Two 'G's is quite a riddle, so please,
One at the start and
None in the middle.

This did not seem to work either. People still put that little extra into our good ship's name. So, we got cunning and started stealing other offenders 'G's and giving them to those without. Thus our two 'chummy' ships, HMS *Bossington* and HMS *Brinton* became the *Bossinton* and *Brington* respectively, and so on with other culprits. That just about stopped it. Mind you, we did draw the line at addressing the Commander in Chief (Fleet) as 'C in C Fleget'. (I wonder if you spotted our 'deliberate mistake'.)

6.   War, Conflict and Time For Reflection

The Cod War of the late 50s and early 60s produced a great deal of publicity for Royal Navy's ships as, bulwarked with wooden fendering and equipped with passive anti-collision rams, they escorted the British fishing fleet on its last great foray. There, in those disputed northern waters, they faced-off the Icelandic gun and patrol boats in an attempt to protect the right of all men to fish the seas. In 1958, Dickie Barr served in the destroyer HMS *Solebay* as part of this Fishery Protection effort. But, what of the fisherman himself? What was his view? How did he feel about it all?

What follows is not a factual account, for such an incident never occurred and no shot was fired; but the possibility of death did haunt the imagination and lay siege to the sleeping hours. Perhaps men started suddenly from their bunks and woke in sweat with trembling limb, wondering what it was that had frightened them. Perhaps it was the shadow to the shadow of their dreams, that lurked unbidden in the void between the conscious and unconscious thought. Perhaps it was this way. On the way to the South Atlantic, years later in that other 'war', the young men of the Task Force had but one real worry. Not 'will I die?' nor 'will I be wounded?' (although these thoughts were not unknown); what concerned them most was 'how will I measure-up, once the shooting starts?'

Although this song was written many years before the 1982 conflict, the sentiments expressed are essentially the same. 'If it happens, how will I turn out?' This is a question that we all must have asked ourselves many a time. This is a question whose answer we can never foresee.

THE COD WAR

Tune: Original

And it's heave away hand over hand ,
Lift the nets. Take the catch to the land.
And it's, split the hull from stem to rudder,
Welcome death with an icy shudder, with an icy shudder.

Our Ship was founded well, foraging food to feed the masses;
The food we gleaned beneath the sea, of many kinds of fishes.
We are not brave men but we are true; To feed so many, we are
but few,
Though many years we've spent braving winds and gales,
To furnish Friday's food to weigh upon the scales.

There were some men who said we stole their livelihood;
By poaching from their seas – that they were just and good,
But these were waters we'd fished for years,
We'd lived with hardships, we'd lived with fears
And we believed that they had been misled,
For the world must eat. The people must be fed.

They pursued us and they cut our nets and tackle.
Bore down upon us, bursting otter-board from shackle.
We had no means nor time to fight.
We ran for fog banks, we prayed for night.
We knew that nations can't exist alone on cattle,
So we waited for the 'Grey' * come and fight our battle.

When a sharp bow comes and with it comes destruction;
When to save your life and your friend's is your only function;
When you shout, 'Hey mate' I see a ship.
'Keep your head up, mate, for death's too quick.'
When you see that ship turn round and change direction,
Then you know – you've tried – you've failed. Your life's gone.

The grey ships, Frigates of the Fishery Protection Squadron

WAR POETRY

NA (Bernie) Bruen

This section contains a personal view of 'war'. Sometimes it is easier to write what one feels in verse than in bald prose and such was the case on the way down to, during and after the Falklands conflict. Moods changed and with them came and went both insight and inspiration. It may be felt that the disparity in styles and content is incongruous, but it should also be remembered that whatever was written, in whatever style, had complete affinity with my situation and I have attempted to recreate the atmosphere of the occasion.

It has often been said that the Royal Navy dislikes individualists – loners, mavericks, free-thinkers – call them what you will; but many people look beyond the normal routines and regimentation and are prepared to speak out for new and better ideas. The Navy tends to ease such people out of the service or perhaps bury them where they will not be 'an embarrassment'. The trouble is that such unconventional people tend to be very good at what they do and, come the conflict, the service looks round in vain for them, wondering where they all went. To quote Commander in Chief Fleet in 1982, when referring to the exploits of the Clearance Diving Teams in San Carlos Water, 'Who are these people? Where do we get them?' Thus it was with some surprise that I was 'dragged out of the woodwork' and sent south in charge of Fleet Clearance Diving Team Three. Mind you, much the same thing can be said of the Clearance Diving Branch as a whole.

TASK FORCE

They don't want us, they want our bodies,
Need our talents, not ourselves.
Conflict calls for dedication,
Expertise enhanced by nerve.

Now ascends the banished Leader,
Outcast of promotion's cull,
Weaving spells of valour's mystic
Vital whisper, 'Follow all!'

But do not bring your conscience;
Do not bring your soul.
The first you'll not be needing;
The second will be stole.

As we progressed southward toward the Total Exclusion Zone, we checked the equipment with which we had been issued. We found that the lifesaving suits that had been given to us were useless and had been slashed and repacked as test cargo for parachute drop training. Someone in stores had got it wrong again. Here is a *shemak* – a sort of extended *tanka* – that muses on the situation.

ON ISSUE WAR STOCK

Slashed Survival-suits
Survived as slashed suits, not as
Suits/(slash)/Survival;
But a slashed Suit (Survival),
As a Survival Suit (slashed),
Survives suitably
To splash below parachutes.

In the early part of the voyage south came reflections on the past and inevitably thoughts of those who had experienced war; whereas we, the sons of warriors, had only played at it.

BEQUEST OF HONOUR

I wonder what our fathers would have thought,
Could they have witnessed sons
Trading on their sires' heroic deeds,
With vehemence of pride,
To heighten their small standing in the school?

For though an undertaking thus discharged,
With little thought for self,
Changes one small section of the whole,
So in transition can
It cause the greater issues to unfold

Thereafter, as the years progress in turn,
To reach along that span,
Growing weaker in its potency,
Yet able still to shape
The course of other actions by and by.

Thus did our fathers' exploits when at war,
Indexed by the ribbons
Proudly borne, bestow upon their heirs
Esteem and rank, conferred
By rule-subjected schoolboy parallels.

How would they think if they could but observe
Those same, if fewer, sons
Take up mantles laid aside in peace
And, never doubting, stride
Away to earn authentic accolades?

There also came a taking stock; a reconciliation and a realisation of where we stood and just what we had to offer; for there was plenty of time to think.

THE ACCOUNT

What do I have to offer my country?
My Services – they are already bought.
My Loyalty – that is understood.
Duty – Honour – were they not always there?
My Enterprise – without it I am nought.
My worldly Worth – would that I had to give.
Love of Country – that was never questioned.
No. What I have is reckoned now to be
But a gesture, an overkill; and yet
Despite the mock, the denigrating words,
I have a Life – and that I volunteer.
No man can offer more.

The closer we came to the battle zone, the more psyched-up we became and, some would say, jingoistic. But, believe me, we meant every word of it. As my 'Sea-dad', Fiddler, said just before we left, 'The Falkands are British – PERIOD!'

THIN OUT

These are our Cousins, peaceful folk.
These are their farms, their sheep, their beef.
Stand then by your mettle (which I doubt).
You have no invitation – thief!
Shout if you like and yell and scream.
Send all your fighters overhead.
Strafe us with bullets, rockets, bombs;
Cripple those ships you coveted.
Or slink and hide and run away,

Cowering behind barbed wire and mines;
Shiver and shake in quaking holes.
Hide in your scant defensive lines.
For it is ours, that earth you dig;
Possess – enjoy it for the day.
Six thousand miles we've come to state,
'The Falklands are British. GO AWAY!'

WE SANCTIONED NO REQUEST

We sanctioned no request from you to claim this land.
You found no warmth nor welcome here,
no friendship's open hand.

We shun that arrogance that brought you to these shores;
You only showed aggression's greed,
to steal what was not yours.

Did we invade your home? Did we close down your schools?
Did we dictate your way of life? Did we impose our rules?

Or did we bolster up your way of life – gone mad,
And did we still regard you for the dignity you had?

Well, We are the British Dead who speak. You are accused!
By us and yours, the men you killed
and those you have abused.

We are the British Dead. We are your slain as well.
We tend the fires that wait for you, within the gates of Hell.

We set up our base by the hospital at Red Beach in San Carlos Water – 'Bomb Alley'. Two things were immediately noticeable; it was almost impossible to tell anyone's rank because badges became lost in the camouflage smocks.

PIPS

Officers' badges,
Frequently indistinct on
Camouflage parkas,
Become buried by action.
Rank holds no structure except
To enhance the spur
Of natural leadership.

And the particular adhesive qualities of the mud in those parts.

MUD

As curved as an Eastern slipper,
The black, glue-like San Carlos peat
Clings to the toe-cap of my boot
And overlays the camouflage
That renders me invisible.

Cracking like a blood-stiff bandage,
Each puttee, steeped in quagmire ooze,
In loosing, shows the cloth beneath
As brightly clean and livid as
The pink of newly healing wounds.

After we were bombed, there were casualties to be buried; but still the wounded came.

AT AJAX BAY

Legs lie crooked, but a fag don't help;
Bodies, shrouded with canvas tenting,
Hastily concealed, yet undisguised,
Struggle in vain for my attention.

Heavily pregnant with wounded men,
Camouflaged Helo's pass overhead,
Darting like birds of prey for the Pad
And the Medics of the Life Machine.

The downdraught tears the air to pieces.
Silent with the casualties' torment
Yet stunned by the engines' agonies,
It sets the ripped tarpaulin flapping.

The silver bodybags start shaking
As if their occupants, awakened
From a horrifying nightmare,
Were in dread panic, thrashing to escape.

Later we shall bury them at dusk,
And, on the hill, a Piper playing
The Flowers of the Forest, gravely,
And with comradeship bid them farewell.

After the bombing, the night was spent in the building of a sandbag blast-wall to protect the operating room and post operation ward from two unexploded bombs lodged in the roof and a refrigeration unit. There seemed to be an endless stream of men, divers mostly, carrying dripping bags of shore gravel through the wards to construct it.

HOSPITAL BLAST-WALL

Softly now and mind your noise.
Don't disturb the wounded boys – sleeping.
Though they dribble down your neck,
Put the sandbags on the deck – weeping.
Use the shingle from the shore.
Bring a couple hundred more – dripping.
Roundly, with a turn belay!

Detonator's on delay – slipping.
Time is short, so lift and haul;
Got to thicken up this wall – stacking.
'Beat the Clock to Beat the Bomb!'
Such a fitting axiom – cracking!
Strip to trousers, boots and belt.
Push yourself until you melt – sweating.
Heave 'em up; no time to lose,
Only minutes on the fuse setting.
Hacked it! – with a bag to spare,
Finest bulwark anywhere – lasting.
Let the sucker detonate;
No way it can penetrate – blasting.

Soon enough the small incidents of the hospital engendered their own verse; a collection that was never finished.

AT THE RED AND GREEN LIFE MACHINE

He was bathing in a pint of tepid water
And shaving in the remnants of his tea.
Coldly standing in a bucket in the passage,
Was the Triage Dental Surgeon's nudity.

Sleeping soldiers packed the corridors and crossings
While Divers dumped the sandbags by the wall
Where an unexploded bomb lodged in the ceiling
And another in the 'frigeration stall.

For a hammock slung between the meat hook girders
Can host a brief, impromptu cabaret
But it is not easy writing home a 'bluie'
When the nearest light is twenty feet away.

With a pocket full of rum and one of whisky,
In a cammy-jacket's mottled brown and green,

Comes the bear-like, three-ring-Surgeon titleholder
Of Rick Jolly's multicoloured Life Machine.

Keep your head down, mate, until this raid is over;
I wouldn't have your job – not if you paid.
Keep your head down, mate, until the night conceals us
Or 'Warning Red' plays 'Yellow's' serenade.

And then there was the imagined conversation to be had with a new arrival; how to explain?

RED BEACH

Yes mate, this is Falkland, find a sangar over there.
Bain't no demarcation, put your kit down anywhere.
Always keep your weapon handy, for the Argies flying low;
Air raids Red and Yellow, anytime, you never know.

That's the Navy Divers' Castle (Called Fort Thompson);
they're all mad,
Though the first to carry in, the wounded from the Pad.
There's a little extra water, seldom any half-way hot;
Medics take what's needed, we can have the stuff that's not.

Them as crouching in the compound,
Argie prisoners, young and cowed,
Live on 'rat-pack' sundries, from the half that we're allowed.
That's a hole made by a bomb
that bounced right here upon the track.
Inside, two more fester, stopping us from moving back.

Yea! that frigate's always waiting,
close inshore like that each day,
Since they bombed us, so's to keep they Argie planes away.
Oh to get there for a dhobi, or perhaps a beer or two!
Well, it's all yours, matey. Keep your head down!
Aye – and you!

The divers helped to care for the wounded, so relieving the medics for more urgent tasks. We all did our share but one incident stood out among all the others. It concerned a sailor who, although badly wounded himself... well judge for yourself.

CASUALTIES

The stretchered sailor, by his friend
Whose hand he clasped and willed his pain to mend,
In whispers to the medics, raised
Imploring eyes, whose sparkle morphine glazed,
Said, 'Help my Oppo, please, not me.
He's hurting bad and worse –
He cannot see.'

Twenty five years later, this poem was chosen as the centrepiece for the RHS Chelsea Flowershow 'Falklands 25' garden exhibit

Although the team received no battle casualties, one man was struck down and almost died.

JOHN-BOY WALTON

(MENTIONED IN DESPATCHES)

They say young John-Boy's
On the danger list;
He'll be lucky to survive.
How bloody stupid,
All the risks he's run,
To be killed by a microbe.
He caught it diving
On a U-X-B,
Next to the sewer.

They say young John-Boy's
In the danger ward
And he's fighting for his life;
Yet, always smiling,
He hugs his trainers
To him, like a talisman.
Come on, John-Boy!
You're our lucky Mascot,
You've got to pull through.

Most of the food that came through Red Beach was dispatched immediately to the front line. What was not was issued to Royal Marine Chef Lenny Carnell, who attempted to feed us all from a single menu, on half rations. After the bombing, Lenny's galley was a shambles and he moved to the other side of the valley, where he fed people only at dawn and dusk. There was only one menu but he did his best with what he had, diverting peoples' attention from the lack of variety by such devious means as inviting the 'Fiddler' to play to the dinner queue and by exhibiting the one and only egg for all to see. He was very good to the divers and sometimes found us that little bit extra. So this is for Lenny.

CHICKEN SUPREME

By crossing the stonefield, into the bog,
And heading en-masse for Len's Café,
At dawn or at dusk, in drizzle or fog,
From vehicles, shelters, secure or unsafe,

Or the shingle-bag sangar we all improvise,
The Royals, the Matelots ask with aplomb,
'So, what have you got for us?' Lenny replies,
'Chicken Supreme and Porn!'

Although it 'comes natural, after a while,
To crave something different... one learns;
From fiddle-tuned dinner queue – Lenny's broad smile
And passing the 'oeuf a'la coque' in the ferns,

For the lifeboat will prosper, and no cause to beg,
With money they threw in the plate for that Prom
But, what was it followed the sight of the egg?
Chicken Supreme and Porn.

A tank landing craft can be fetid and cold,
Abandoned without any power;
While UXBs, shifted by chain-hoist, I'm told,
Can hold one's attention for hour after hour;

But the candle-lit quiz, when invited to dine,
Since lifting and shifting the thousand pound bomb,
'What feast can we have with that bottle of wine?'
'Chicken Supreme and Pom.'

'Chicken Supreme and Porn.' says he,
'A spoonful of each; that's your lot.
'There ain't nothing else, apart from the tea,
'But it's tasty, nutritious and hot!'

Four of us were sent to Bluff Cove to check out the still-burning *Sir Tristram* and *Sir Galahad* for unexploded ordnance. Whilst we searched *Tristram*, Jock and Whiskey up forward, Tommo and me back aft, unbelievably, others from our own side were stealing our gear from the upper deck. But, if ever there was one, this is a true 'heart-beat' poem.

TRISTRAM AT THE COVE

It was all too easily definite.
All it required was to take our kit
Into a twisted ship and climb

Ladders and walkways, a step at a time,
Down and through her cavernous bowels,
Ignoring the damage's groans and growls,
Past the engines, looming and damp,
With only the warmth of a battery lamp,
Hanging from girders blackened with soot,
Gauging the strength of the plates underfoot,
Thoroughly, doggedly, further apart,
When all you can hear is the beat of your heart,
Finding the source of the havoc to know
That nothing else lurked and was waiting to blow,
Cautiously peering in corners to see,
Silently searching – Tommo and me.

When 'Tommo' and I boarded *Galahad*, all was chaos and there
was little we could do for her. But we did cover over the body of
a young soldier who had not survived the onslaught. This
incident affected us deeply. We could not help the ship and were
too late to aid the man. We went away heavy-hearted.

TO A YOUNG GALAHAD

Naked is no way to die, nor yet to lie,
Frozen in the act of living;
At first I thought you caught in spasm,
Locked into a callisthenic dorsal arch,
Muscles – shoulder, thigh and arm – straining with the effort.
Then I saw your face half burned away to show
The grin of teeth that lies beneath the skin,
Your fingers turned to stubby stumps, and dog-tags gone;
Only your boots and one arm thrust into a shirt
marked your haste to leave.
(Did you once sun yourself, running your hand
Lazily over some girlfriend's thigh,
As she in turn smoothed oil upon your back?)

Somehow you died whole, unbroken
Until you tumbled to that griddle deck
That burned and scorched and seared,
Welding you to it.

Who was the man who caused your death?
Was he like those who yesterday pilfered through our kit,
While we hunted bombs and rockets, Deep in a dying ship?
Your ship is dying too, burning,
rumbling to the explosions that,
Rock the pall of blackened flames. I cannot help her.

Excuse me if I leave you now,
But there are jobs to do and fires to fight.
Snow is in the air and bleakness coming with the winter wind.
Although you can feel nothing,
yet this tarp will keep away the chill
And clothe you for a while from prying, vulture eyes.
I leave you with your ship to guard
as you have done in lonely vigil;
But I will tell them where you lie.
And, if tardily, someone will come to tend you.

In 2012 I was in Stamford being filmed for a documentary for
Channel 5, a British TV station. It was about the bomb disposal
effort we put in during the Falklands war. All was going smoothly and well until the moment I was telling what we found
onboard Galahad at Bluff Cove. Unaccountably and very
suddenly, when I was explaining about the young soldier we
found welded to the deck, I burst into uncontrollable sobbing –
something I swore I would never do and, indeed, had never
done since the war. I had to turn away and it was several
minutes before I was able to continue. Perhaps it takes thirty
years and the intensity of filming to relive the events and to

finally react to them. Anyhow, it affected me greatly and, shortly afterwards, I wrote the poem below.

TO A YOUNG GALAHAD – THIRTY YEARS ON

They brought their screens and smoke machines,
An HD camera and a Dolby mike
And, with a wooden bomb, a working fuze,
Selective lighting and some drapes,
Transformed my kitchen to a bombed-out ship
And said, "Tell us again what it was like."

I told them of the Galahad;
Of how we saved her that first, frightful night
When, from an acid-saturated wreck
That burned the clothing from our skin,
We worked to free a sleeping bomb and so
Return her life, so nearly brought to waste.

I told them of the Lancelot;
Of how we cut apart her gangways, worked
The night, and through the raids that terrorised
The day, to lift and shift and heave
And haul a dormant bomb from deep within
Until we could return her to the Fleet.

I told them, then, about Bluff Cove;
Of how we battled with the Tristram blaze,
The four of us, to save her too – too late -
And blasted off her after door
So they could salvage shells and mortar-bombs,
Munitions for the hungry, Stanley guns.

And then again of Galahad
Who rocked and burned a pall of blackened flame
That rose from glowing bulkheads, blistered decks,
A signal column, dark above;
And you – for whom we could do nothing more
Than find a piece of canvas for a shroud.

Thirty years too late, unbidden,
Unexpected, unashamed, with sudden
Overflowing eyes, my message faltered;
For, though you never were forgot,
You're long past due those tears I shed for you;
As, in bewilderment, I turned away – and so did they.

We were back in the area a little later when, having 'captured' a live, horned sea mine and contrived to beach it ashore; we were invited to take it apart and find out how it worked – defusing it in the process. Unfortunately we had not been allowed to bring with us from UK the five boxes of specialist kit specially designed to do this sort of thing, it being considered that:

a) we would not need it;

b) that it was too valuable to take into a war zone and

c) (unbelievably) someone else might have need of it!

What price a man's life, eh? It was also interesting to be informed by satellite link that experts at home were convinced that the device was fitted with anti-stripping gadgets – booby-traps. Consequently the mind was racing the night before and the realisation was that the odds were not good. This task was to be, by necessity, a one man affair and the 'Boss' was, by definition, that man.

APOGEE

Sing no sad songs for me if I come second in tomorrow's race;
The opposition, mine to leave, could,
with deception, all my skill outpace.
Play no lament for me if I misread the signals of the game;
The steadiness I must achieve, should,
with attainment, stay the waiting flame.
Shed no soft tears for me if I am

vanquished in the coming bout;
The uppercut I might receive would
far surpass the ultimate knockout.

The operation was a success and the mine was returned to England and the Naval Museum. Now that the conflict was over, the staff officers arrived from UK 'to put things in perspective and back to normal'. I expect that they felt out of things and compensated by bluster and pontification. Some of them tended to be very good at 'transmitting' but had no wish to 'receive'.

THE SENIOR LEACH

Should we remark, 'How right you are.'
Or with forthrightness say,
'Despite mistakes we may have made,
It was not done that way.

No doubt you will hypothesize,
Our actions to decry,
But it was us who made the grade.
It was not you – t'was I.'

We listen, dutifully bound,
As younger men must do,
While condescending patronage,
Our comments honeydew.

Perhaps he's right, this pedagogue,
Pretentious, unconcerned,
But he had never seen that wreck,
From which we had returned.

So, when that breeze of platitudes
Increases to a gale,

When he, unknowing of our part,
Creates some fairytale-

Of our attainments, using me,
As springboard to his rank,
I muse, 'You swill your brandy, pal,
But it was rum we drank.'

Unaware of our history or endeavours and not a bit interested it
seemed, some of these people snorted and scoffed and called us
'cowboys'. They were unconcerned that we had only the clothes
we stood up in, all our spares going to the survivors of the Bluff
Cove incident, and voiced their opinions whenever they felt the
need. It seemed that they resented our easy familiarity with our
counterparts in the SAS and Commando. The conflict being
over, the 'oddballs' were being shown the door again.

This poem is our reply, in the place of the silence we kept at
the time.

WE ARE THE COWBOYS

We are the Cowboys. I've heard you say it loudly in the bar
Although, well hidden by the smoke of your cigar.
We are the Cowboys, because our hair's too long
and our uniform is wrong;
We are the Cowboys, in spite of our success
and 'coz of wearing gymshoes in the Mess.

We are the Cowboys. It must be so, 'coz Staff are never wrong.
You do not know us – but we'll jolly you along.
We are the Cowboys, a denigrating word
to make us seem absurd;
We are the Cowboys, because we wear no rank
and hold that certain 'Johnny-Lates' are dank.

We are the Cowboys, you think that sailors
should be awed and cowed
But we dare to be different – and that ain't allowed.
We are the Cowboys, because we are 'alive',
and that we Clearance Dive;
We are the Cowboys, we have unique rapport,
and talk with 'Super-Secrets' and the Corps.

We are the Cowboys, and I suspect you'll quash us if you can;
You have the Admiral's ear. You are the Precious Man.
We are the Cowboys, you make that very clear
to anyone who'll hear.
We are the Cowboys, because we look so 'bad'
but what do you know of the Jobs we've had?

And then we came home – all of us – safely. Looking back over
the whole episode in analytical form, it seemed that we had
come close to oblivion on several occasions. We were none of us
the same people who had set out to war, we had been to the
Limit of Life, peered over and returned with:

THE VIEW FROM THE EDGE

Peering from a Landing Craft stuck in the kelp,
Watching an air-raid filled with Rapier flares,
Ducking as the bullets flatten overhead;

Scrutinizing tension in a cable hoist,
Contorting, wrestling with a thousand pounder,
Waiting for the 'click' of its fuse 'going live';

Squinting at the brightness of molten metal
Showering from the bulkhead being cut away,
Wetting down the weapon to put out the flames;

Glimpsing the underside of a plane at dusk
Shrieking low over the hospital building,
Hearing its bombs detonating all around;

Seeking the route through a twisted skeleton,
Swinging above the smoulder of shipborn fires,
Hefting weighty explosives in a backpack;

Scanning bulkheads glowing in a burning ship,
Feeling explosions stagger the hull beneath,
Covering a body – welded to the deck;

Finning backwards in a breaking wave at sea,
Fending off a mine, a beachball in the surf,
Recoiling from horns that one must not bend;

Reaching, later, in amongst its circuits, while,
Viewing the stillness of the Falkland evening,
Musing on the detonator; right or left?

Here and here the Limits are.
Here the Unknown is revealed.
It is the View from the Edge.

Of the 18 men who set off to go 'down south', twelve were awarded official recognition, either by being Mentioned in Dispatches, given Commander-in-Chief's Commendations or Gallantry Awards. But beware the publicity that accompanies such things.

FAME

Solitude's mantle,
Ripped apart by the grasping
Fingers of the mob,
Although retrieved in tatters,
Offers no sanctuary

To shroud our secrets
Nor yet our imperfections.

Some four years later I went back to the Islands for a tour of duty. During that time we recovered the remains of an Argentinian pilot from the rocky hinterland.

BLUE RIDGE PILOT

It is a strange feeling to take a man's hand
In pieces from the peat where it has lain four years,
Scraping his finger bones from the frozen ground
With a bayonet point, to stack them neatly aside.

How odd it is to find his hair still ruffled
In that rocky cranny where the cold wind explores,
And to glean scattered bones, left by the scavengers,
Seeking to catalogue his percentage presence.

The wreckage of his plane tells us how he peered
Through the blizzard, to see the ridge looming above;
How he might have cleared the scarp, but for the rock,
The outcrop that became his natural tombstone.

But rather than relate the tale, now he makes
His bed in the cold earth of Goose Green Cemetery.
Yet there is another, pleasanter feeling,
To know that at last his long vigil is over.

Then came the Gulf War of 1991...

CICADAS

Cicadas, chirping blithely in acacia trees,
Know nothing of war, until the instant they are
Shrivelled by its searing flame
And that resounding
Song becomes their epitaph.

JANUARY 1991 – MEDIA GAMES

Now is the battle-roar of tanks
seen to splash through shallows in the sands.
Now is the smell of victory,
tangent from a box within our hands.
Now is the pilot viewed,
loosing smarter weapons into foreign lands.
Now is the Soldier's spousal tear watched in close-up,
as the News demands.
Now is triumph squeezed, ('Take – seven!')
From the Fighter, warlike as he stands.
Now is used the replay function,
Haunting TV's colour channel bands.

A soldier wrote about the carnage and destruction that was the Battle of the Somme in the Great War, 'This was a time when a web was woven across the sky, and a Goblin made of the Sun.' The sheer size of the destruction and harm done to the ecology of the area made the brief hostilities in the Gulf comparable. But wherever there is conflict, the same may be said. Think back to HMS *Antelope* at San Carlos, the Hospital at Ajax Bay and *Galahad* at Bluff Cove.

GULF WAR 1991

And in those days a tangled veil
Was drawn across the sky.
A madness, kindled in the sun
(made Goblin there withal),
Convulsed and gibbered in its rage
To light inhuman pyres.
Now, squatting with a rancid grin,
This spawn of incubi
Bestirred the earth with turbulence,
Awoke a tainted squall
And conjured up the retching smoke
Of high-explosive fires.
So demons, deep in artifice,
Bestow their gifts – supply
The oily dust to choke and burn
But, in that reeking pall,
The Goblin meets a darker shroud
And, every night, expires.

Service in HMS *Albion*, a Commando ship (see 'Life is Really Super for the Booties'), brought Bernie Bruen, for the first time in contact with Royal Marines and the aircraft that ferried them about. The fascination I had then was in the 'soul' of these machines: for they have a soul, as does a ship. I mused upon their many differing roles, their communion with those who flew them, whom they flew and those who might one day try and stop them flying. This last group divides into two:

a) the Enemy of War – who ever that might one day be, and

b) the Enemy in High Places – whose job appears to be to put a stop to anything worthwhile and useful, all in the cause of economy. Perhaps it was just us, the users, who could actually 'feel' these machines, talk to them and understand them. Perhaps we were the only ones who really cared.

ODE TO A COMMANDO HELICOPTER

Oh wingless bird that rents the air,
Transporting men of war
Or bringing succour to the needful few,
Wherein lies your power?
Oh wingless bird that rents the air,
What makes you so assured
That you will never fall toward the sea?
Therein lies your power.

Oh heart forever beating hard,
When will you pause for rest?
Will you outlive your body's brittle strength, and
Is your story told?
Oh innocence that crawls inside,
Does war your prison make
Or do you find a peacefulness benign
Deep within her hold?

Oh, hawk that waits upon the shore
And crouches with intent,
Are you placated with a single death?
How much will you dare?
Oh patriot and those at home,
Is interest all you feel
And do you see the good that's wrought?
Do you really care?

Oh wingless bird that rents the air,
Transporting men of war,
Your beauty is far more than you can tell,
To any in the Corps.

❖ ❖ ❖

TIME FOR REFLECTION

It was a splendid evening in Gerry Kingdom's old Cornish cottage, when Bill Seymour, Fiddler Jennings and I were his guests for supper. Outside was a cold and blustery winter's darkness. The rain rattled against the cottage windows in gusts of assault while the malevolent wind drew tunes from the chimney breast. The firelight bathed the ceiling beams of old ships' timbers in a golden glow and, half seen, amid the fireplace stone winked little 'treasures', set there by its builder, Poet and Shellback, Bernie Skuse, to delight the finder's eye: a broken clay pipe, a piece of coral, an old coin and the smallest ship-in-a-bottle imaginable. A finer company of like- minded souls and a cosier haven would have been hard to find. We had eaten well of a meal and such trimmings as would share the dish, including some of Bill's specially burned onions for 'better health', and had settled back, draped across sofa and overstuffed armchair, to proceed quietly around the world a time or two in the company of some good Cornish ale. As the subjects turned and flowed the conversation chanced upon the songwriter's art and what it took to find the Muse.

Amid such reverie, Bill and I decided, then and there, that now was just the time to combine our talents and awake that elusive 'spirit' to our needs. Later, when the song was finished, Bill declared himself a little tired and made his way upstairs to bed. There I went to see him, before I left and took my road to Scotland, taking him a pint of Hicks Ale, emergency rations for the night. I never saw him again, for he died before many days were past. Here now is his last song.

TEARS

Bill Seymour and Bernie Bruen

When I was but a tender lad, my Daddy said to me,
'Tis only little boys that cry, for grown men don't, you see.'
But why do sons of men cry out, what pain or anguish know
Compared with that their elder kin, had suffered years ago?

For few and many are the times,
that cause the tears to start,
When men of stature, power and strength
will shake with broken heart.
A ship we've known is left to rot;
a friend lies dead in war;
An ancient man, who once was young,
lies destitute and poor.

The Royal Pageant music plays;
the bird with broken wings;
All these can cause the heart to fail.
A boy can't see these things.
So should a child get used to tears
and use them in his youth
Or save them for his adult years,
Reality and Truth?

The legendary Valhalla of all sailors, fishermen in particular, is Fiddlers Green. When our time is done, the last course charted, the steering set and our ship of life is sailing full and bye towards that final haven, perhaps these thoughts will ease our passing. This poem has been read at the funerals of many ex sailors, from Able Seamen to Admirals. It is a fitting epitaph for anyone who has ever lived at sea.

APPROACH TO THE GREEN

I look across the chart that is my life and see,
like ports and harbours,
Little creeks and streams, all the happy times
and oft' the ones of strife
That filled me with a joy of living and of dreams.
Yet many, lying soft like pools of misty grey,
But half remembered, never whole and clear to see,
Quietly unnoticed, slide away
And softly lock their doors and hide away the key.

No more shall they be seen, nor bide with me, that others
share what
I still know they are. Like unknown shadow shapes of eventide
They fly, they fade in misty dreams afar.
And as I drift and let life slide me by,
So one by one each hatch is shut and locked and barred,
'Till only one direction, one last door I spy
And there a shining figure, sword in hand, stands guard

For one reason or another (probably because I upset someone) I found myself on the remote island of Diego Garcia, a thousand miles from the nearest mainland and a mere four feet above sea level, with a year's 'penal servitude' from the Navy to complete. The island, the largest in the British Indian Ocean Territories (BIOT), is not that big and in 1979 contained 2000 American servicemen and 35 Brits. I was Chief of Police. I had a very nice Jeep with a flashing blue light on top, which I used to chase the drivers of dumpsters who broke the 15mph speed limit. I had to buy my own 'dee-dah', though. Actually, it was the epitome of a tropical paradise and I very much enjoyed my 'sentence'. It was during that time that I wrote this most favourite of my poem/songs.

A SAILOR'S DREAM OF DEVON

Bernie Bruen

To Plymouth I was bound, one clear and frosty day.
I loaded sleeping-bag and tent and soon was on my way.
The miles passed one by one, they mounted score on score
And as they vanished in the dusk,
I thought the more and more
Of Devon far away.

And when I reached the end of that half a thousand miles,
My pulse a-race, my eyes a-shine, my face awash with smiles,
The happy hours passed quickly and the memory will remain
But every parting broke my heart and made me long again
For Devon far away.

We sailed the rippling Sound and walked the Dartmoor hills.
We camped beneath the winter sky when all the world was still
And every jar of ale and every pub we knew
Engraved the letters on my heart, for now I know it's true;
That Devon's far away.

And now, though half the world between us surely lies,
A day is never passing but my mind to Devon flies.
If I perchance am homesick, caught a-luff, becalmed, in stays
Then let me languish under that strange illness all my days,
If Devon's far away.

Oh Devon, far away, the land where I would go;
The places where the music will enliven every heart;
Where the friendship of a few, Means more than they will know;
Where journeys have their ending,
But where all of mine must start.

The Middle Watch at sea on a calm, starlit night, with one's little ship (or greater one) smoothly following her charted course, is a time for thought and reflection.

SEA-NIGHT

When seas are quiet, winds are soft,
Nor stirs the muffled flag aloft;
When shadows gather each to each,
And seagulls sing in muddy reach;
When lights go out and, tail to nose,
The dolphins, never stirring, warmly doze;
When half across a darkening sea,
Awesome tales return to you and me;
When well below a cool, kind covering of slime,
The water dwellers feast on food sublime;
When iron grinds not on iron, nor steel on steel,
And everything we know becomes unreal;
When eyelids flicker, breathing stills,
And even fishes rest their gills;
Then, though we neither hear nor see,
The world, for which we think we hold the key,
Wakes once again and, as we sleep, is free.

The ocean can be a hostile place and any man venturing thereon does so without the certain knowledge that he will return safely to land. Some spend almost their whole lives at sea – fishing or trading. Others answer their country's call and fight bloody war upon the waves. Yet others brave the most appalling conditions to pluck near- lost souls from the peril of the storm. But ask any man why he goes to sea and, despite the rhetoric of the years, he will not be able to say. There is a force that pulls a person to sea just as surely as it beckons many more to its strand to watch and marvel. The land is our sure refuge from all the gales and tempests that ever raged; yet sometimes that too can play us false.

When we get too close, or careless, or just too sure of ourselves, then the land will ally with the sea and leave us wrecked, washed up and dying. Small wonder that every seaman knows where is the safest place in a storm – well out from the land, with plenty of sea room.

'A ship can be safe in harbour but belongs at sea.'
Shihab Tariq

But when land and sea combine to give us brutal reminders of their dread power; when they try to squeeze us between themselves, waves crashing on rock or bar and the poor cockle-shell not knowing which way lies salvation; then it is that the men of the Royal National Lifeboat Institute who pit their knowledge, strength and skill against the flood to pluck a life from such assaults. They are the men, landsmen or seamen, who heed the maroon – the call to danger; men of stature, men of strength, men of dedication. So, next time you see a 'lifeboat', pass not by before you put a little of what you can spare to help these doughty sailors, heroes all, the Men of the Sea.

MEN OF THE SEA

What men are these who ply the seas,
what forms of self-destruction?
What living symbols of our fate,
what victims of reduction?
What right is given them to kill,
what right for preservation?
What right to take a human life,
what price its conservation?

What knowledge do they use for good,
what knowledge use for evil?
What acts can help? What acts can harm?
What homage pays the devil?
And when will they be free again
and will they be contented?
And will they have the life they choose
or will they be prevented?

And is the rocky land a curse
or is it just depressing?
And have they left their God behind
or do they ask his blessing?
So, is the sea their only world
or is the land their ally?
Or do they wish to turn again,
And thus repent their folly?

Are they pure kindred to the sea
or are they souls tormented?
And do they speak their mind out loud,
And is their case presented?
The answers, they cannot be told.
The questions... answered never.
They are the men who search the seas.
Their quest goes on for ever.

7. RECREATION

There are many opponents of amateur boxing and much is blazoned and blared in the media that condemns it as a violent and inhuman sport. Rest assured that the people who make these noises have never stepped inside a boxing ring to fight for a championship nor to represent their fellows. Boxing's opponents have never experienced the magic of the sport and cannot possibly appreciate its attraction, nor the hold it exercises over the participants. No matter how they spout and waffle, no matter how good they are with words or arguments, they simply do not know. They are outsiders. They are but spectators. They do not have the stance, the guard, the skill. They are not boxers.

For many years, in the 1970s and 80s, the Royal Navy held sway in amateur boxing and had many famous names to its credit. Some naval boxers went on to earn professional championships, even to become Champion of the World; all were the best of fellows and Bernie was lucky enough to be part of that squad. From International Class, boxers like Paul Kelley, Terry Marsh and Nicky Croombes – to such as Gordon McBride, whose 'heart' was bigger than anyone's – they were all giants of their time and a tribute to those two great Navy coaches, Tony Oxley and Mickey Shone. This song was written for clearance diver Tommy 'Buck' Taylor, who was one of the bravest and most able light heavyweights of his day. It probably comes as close as anything could to explain what it is about boxing that captures our hearts, and gives us such pride in those three words emblazoned on the holdall – ROYAL NAVY BOXING. Certainly there has been a copy of the song displayed in the RN boxing gym since it was written in 1977.

LIGHT HEAVY

Take a strong aggressive pose,
With forehead lowered, spring in toes,
The left hand poised to strike with speed,
The right in check, in case of need,
The body set on steady feet,
Belief in skill without defeat,
Your breathing steady, eyes aflame,
Thoughts on moves to win the game.

The lights, reflected from below,
Reveal the scars of long ago
Ahead of you he stands
As calm as feelings will allow
And you and he will win and lose
And you and he will have to choose
The time is when, the method how.
The place is here, the time is – now!

With flowing blood and broken nose,
You stand with right eye swollen closed
With well-bruised torso, muscles strained,
You know you'd do it all again
But cannot tell you why.
No pain could show you where to stop
No well-aimed blows could gain the top,
You fought with spring and boundless strength,
Until the time arrived at length,
To rest you by and by.

No hatred can you harbour now,
No hatred had you ever vowed
T'was just your skill against his own,
T'was just as though you're all alone

And only you to care.
The ring, the battleground you used
Is empty, shining, win or lose,
With blood of contest, now or then,
It stands for use by special men,
Where most would never dare.

The Joint Services Mountain Training Centre at 'Tywyn' in North Wales hatched its own clutch of songs, sketches and skits that the young sailors, soldiers and airmen performed at end-of-course concerts (Sod's Operas). After a hard three weeks of Outward Bound training, their humour mirrored their pride of achievement, having experienced hitherto unknown adventures and succeeded where they felt sure they must fail. This is one of the few that survived from the many that were written and fell Bernie's way as the instructor in charge of organising the entertainment.

TYWYN

Bernie Bruen

It's a wonderful place, it is, Tywyn,
When you get here you have a great time
For the rain never rains upon Tywyn ,
And the sun in the sky always shines.

When you go for a walk in the bundoo,
With your rucksack and karrimat too
You'll all get that proud sort of feeling;
If the fog lifts there's quite a nice view.

When your tent blows away up on Snowdon,
And you're left there alone in your 'sack',
Just run to a barn and then whistle;
If you're lucky, your tent will come back.

The beach rocks are slippery and slimy,
The same thing for all who come here
But d'you know, to my way of thinking,
You've all come at the wrong time of year.

Most of the time the sea's placid,
Not many waves break on the shore
Except for when you lot go swimming,
And then they're – what, – ten foot or more.

So make sure you don't break your thermos,
And don't lose your can of spare fuel
Keep your map dry, neat and tidy,
And they'll ask you to teach at the School.

Fifty years ago, the Royal Navy Kayak Association (RNKA) was made up of a small number of dedicated canoeists who used their best endeavours to turn up, when sea-time permitted, in a motley collection of private vehicles, to any competition they could reach. Not for the Navy was the system, adopted by the Army and RAF, of full support, time off and training for the teams of paddlers. The members of the RNKA were on their own time and resources. More often than not, a couple or three Navy boys would meet by the rapids on the day of the event and form an instant team. Their much patched-and-mended kayaks were eyed coldly by the soldiers and airmen who, resplendent in uniform tracksuits and watching from regimented, tented camps, had been ensconced there for a fortnight or more, training hard for the event.

Shiny canoes, the newest gear, cook tent, latrines, white-washed stones, flagpole and strategically placed groups of fire extinguishers were the hallmarks of these fortunate young men. Masking tape, angle-iron roof-racks, Mars bars and home-made wet suits were those of the Navy boys; yet the matelots still managed to win the trophies, much to the chagrin of their brothers-in-arms.

This song was written by Bernie, to cheer us all up in the face of the opposition and our own Service's indifference to our sport. The original version of this song was written by that most remarkable of people – Charles Saunders. Marksman, musician, Naval Officer, rally driver, martial arts expert, sailor, poet, songwriter, composer, canoeist and solicitor – he was all set to turn Hereford's Sea Cadet Unit, TS VAGA (of which he was Commanding Officer) into the National Canoe headquarters, when he was cruelly struck down by some dread internal illness that brought such activities to a premature conclusion. However, he does have an unrivalled collection of original canoeing and drinking songs.

PADDLERS

(Bernie Bruen) Tune: A Policeman's Lot

I'm a paddler, I go paddling in the water,
'Whether green or white or blue I cannot tell,
With my crash-hat, knee-bars, buoyancy and spraydeck
And my 'oppo' in his kayak, all is well.

We 'pop-out', 'loop' and 'pearl-dive' in the dumpers
And we don't worry, for we know that soon
We will change from wet suits into jeans and jumpers
And we'll drink to surfing all the afternoon.

We compete long-distance races, sprints and slalom;
Go paddling down the rapids with aplomb,
And we've got a corner cupboard full of prizes
We have won for races short and rough and long.

We've got the newest of the K2 racers
And we're building three new boats in our front room
And when we're done we'll put them through their paces
And we'll drink to racing all the afternoon.

You may ride the raging green-back to the breakers.
You may 'pop-out' with a pirouette or two
And perhaps you'll use a 'paddle-brace' to finish
When you're surfing, in your slalom-type canoe.

We go out and do this every Sunday
And the public come and watch us from the dunes;
Then we'll win the National Championship one day
And we'll drink to all those Sunday afternoons.

When we use a 'hanging-draw' or 'cross-bow-rudder',
Breaking in and out of stoppers, shoots and falls,
Use 'Colorado hook', 'high-cross' or 'J' stroke,
Every other paddler stands right up and calls,

'Oh, you're the best canoeists on the rivers,
'To the kayak world you are the greatest boon;
'Of technique and style you are the knowledge-givers
'And we'll buy you drinks all through the afternoon.'

This is a cautionary tale for canoeists that was written after a very interesting descent of the wild 'River Findhorn – at night.' This memorable trip was undertaken by the instructors of the Moray Outward Bound School, of which Bernie was one, in the summer of 1972. His kayak developed a fault in the spraydeck fastening and he was unable to continue to the finish as it constantly filled up with water. The only way out of the particular gorge he was in was a fascinating rock-scramble up a cliff – with his canoe. Unfortunately, on reaching the top the bow lanyard parted and gravity took over. Next day they retrieved the boat from the bottom of a deep pool and nailed the five –

remaining pieces above the Canoe Store door as a dreadful warning to all. That trip suggested this song, which is in itself apocryphal.

THE ROLLING SONG

Bernie Bruen Tune: The Threshing Machine

I got out my kayak to go for a trip.
I paddled away at a hell of a clip.
I paddled off downstream all on my own
And, in view of what happened, I wish I'd stayed home.

I descended the first fall, my landing was poor;
Went into a rapid of grade five or more
And I thought to myself how I wished I had looked
At the route through the rapid, for my goose was cooked.

There were stoppers and races and rips and whirlpools.
I wished I'd remembered the first of the rules;
Don't go canoeing alone if you wish
To stay hale and hearty not food for the fish.

My bow was sucked into a cauldron of foam.
I had no one to help me, was all on my own.
The stern was cracked up to the seat on my left
And the bow was thrust into a waiting rock cleft.

A stopper appeared where it should not have been.
It wasn't a white one – but threateningly green.
It gave me a twist to the right and I saw
That I'd have to try rolling or else something more.

I tried a 'paulata' but to no avail.
I tried for a 'screw' but that too did fail.
My 'steyer' is weak and my 'put-across' nil
So I pulled off the spraydeck and watched my boat fill.

Five pieces, five pieces is all I have left;
A seat and a kneebar and half a foot-rest.

I shudder, now, telling this story to you.
That's all that remains of my shattered canoe.

A roll can be seen by both beggars and kings
But seeing and doing are two different things;
With cocked-wrist and hip-flick and angle of blade,
You soon will discover the 'horlicks' you've made.

(Thanks again to Charles Saunders for the basic song.)

Another view of that endless battle between the elements and the land must be seen from 'weather's' point of view. With only a transient connection to the all-powerful sea, a weaker, more temporary member of the troops arrayed against the earth, the rain's attack is but short-lived. Soon it flows away, back to the waters whence it came. But with it comes a strange story. Yet again that turncoat creature, late of the water-world, makes his play. This time, in seeming pointless effort, he cavorts upon the flood, as though taunting it to greater efforts. How can this be understood, how explained? The water sees nothing to be gained, no feint or purpose to such darting attacks. It is disturbed for, try as it might, it cannot claim a prisoner to carry off to the deep where the answer can be found.

THE SLALOM

'The water falls from clouds of foam.
It tumbles down where speed is sure
And ends its journey with the shock
Of falling 'gainst the solid rock.

The separate drops unite again.
They run together, join their hands
And show their pleasure in the sight
Of friends and neighbours from the sky.

And so this happy merry throng,
Unsure of where the journey ends
Proceeds on exploration bent,
On rights before undreamed.

As they journey on their way,
Others join and then still more,
Until they form a steady stream,
The leaders led by those behind.

Unknown to these already met
Are others with the "single thought";
The thought of wandering through a land
Already seen but never felt.

These others, like the ones we know,
Converge and meet our gentle few
And form a river with the power
To move a mountain with the years.

But something's changed. They're not the same.
They've lost their purpose and they rush,
A mad and senseless crowd who think
No thoughts – their minds are dumb.

And yet they have the wherewithal!
To see the creature that we call a man
Do battle with their teeming souls,
As though he plays a senseless game.

'They fight him with their mightiest rage
And use their meanest, cunning sense
To camouflage Man's allied friend
And turn him to distrust and fear.

They cause an uprush of themselves,
Quickly followed by a void
And hope that this enraged support
Will foil the cockle, his protection.

But though they try with every strength,
They cannot comprehend the thought
Of Man within his cockle shell
That sees them as enjoyment.

And so they struggle, push and fight,
E'en though their enmity is lost.
They know that Man cannot be beat
Despite his death or injury.

As they have started,
So they cannot stop,
As the others far behind
Force them ever onwards,
Faster. 'Til, 'The waterfalls form clouds of foam.'

8.   HUMOUR

The Royal Navy, like the other branches of the armed services, is a naturally humorous place. Men, and latterly women too, living in close proximity with each other, facing uncertainty, danger and lengthy periods away from their loved ones, tend to relieve the tension this produces through humour and wit. Most all of the other chapters in this book contain items of humour, and it is right that they should. We have only created this chapter for those efforts that do not sit easily with the themes of other chapters.

A REPLY FOR THE LADIES

It is always a little difficult to make a speech on behalf of the guests aboard ship on Ladies Night, but you may find this one suitable for this and similar occasions, perhaps with a word changed here and a phrase there. The speech is short and to the point, although the point is sometimes a little difficult to ascertain, and makes a nice change from the usual pleasantries passed in after dinner speeches.

> *'It is not often that one such as I, is given the opportunity of replying on behalf of the Ladies. However, the opportunity has been presented; I am here and I shall reply. One should, it is true, prepare oneself a worthy plaudit for such an occasion – an occasion so beset by the larger standards that the caution exercised must be of conjecture, not peremptory skill. Therefore, with that in mind and without further respite, without prevarication or delay – delay that could cause doubt within, without doubt – within that*

doubt and without doubting the delay, I shall doubtless not delay but proceed.

'Where, we must ask ourselves, is the connection between this feast, that we have just endured – enjoyed, and the celebration of the appropriate day we presently remember? This is surely a wide question and one that must be asked of us all. Are we to liken it to the myths remembered only in the unresponsive corners of a nether intellect? If so, why pause for reaction? I'm sorry, I'll say that again. If so, why? (pause for reaction). Where is the relevance of such untrammelled facings when imposed upon the whole morass of fragmented ambiguity? These are also questions, not so wide – it is true, but questions none the less.

But, as we all know, the reply on behalf of the Ladies originates from the celebration of that finest of all Scottish Romantics – Nobby Burns – whose brother, Rabbie, achieved some little fame. Who can forget his immortal lines upon this subject? There is no need to repeat them here, for are they not seared into the very fibres of our memories? Do they not run, tripping, skipping, helter skelter, lighter than the gossamer itself, through our very beings? Of course they do. Well, maybe for the sake of the youngsters – perhaps just a few lines from this, his most famous and celebrated work – which, you will agree, says it all:

Aye, away the Feemell grows,
An' follows doon the Glen, a-mair.
Notch yer wee Akhrooder-mor ,
That, bleedin', falls a-neath the hare.
Shno' the bricht fair limpid pool,
Shnae the Brakle-mundie's grin,
Brought to few yon Kirkle-grue,
That beats the Braggard breast within.
Beware the Wimpril-Lassie, Mon!
Keep yer Breekers twixt yer knees;

Or else the Feemell-Trokht will come,
And fairly give yer Loure a squeeze.'

Every sailor enjoys a 'Run Ashore' and more often than not arrives back aboard ship in one piece. However, there are dangers lurking in seaports both at home and abroad, for the unwary. Based upon a popular song of the era, this little ditty describes the versatility of manual communication.

'Three for what you owe me' was Jack's indication of a large tot of Rum. Ask a sailor and he will demonstrate. But it will cost you a 'Pussers'.

THE BUNCH OF FIVES

Tune: Bunch of Thyme

Come all you Matelots far and near,
All you with sweethearts and with wives,
Take care and more,
When on a run ashore,
Not to stop a bunch-of-fives.

For 'fives' are very special things
And many meanings can portray;
One's for 'up your nostril'
And three for what you owe me
And two for 'won't you go away!'

Sir Henry Newbolt's marvellous poem 'Drake's Drum' is part of our National Heritage and stirring stuff it is too. I reproduce it here in case you missed it last time around.

DRAKE'S DRUM

Drake he's in his hammock an' a thousand miles away,
(Capten, art tha' sleepin' there below?)
Slung atween the round shot in Nombre Dios Bay,
An' dreamin' arl the time o' Plymouth Hoe.

Yarnder lumes the Island, yarnder lie the ships,
Wi' sailor lads a-dancin' heel-an'-toe,
An' the shore-lights flashin', an' the night-tide dashin',
He sees et art so plainly as he saw et long ago.

Drake he was a Devon man, an' ruled the Devon seas,
(Capten, art tha sleepin' there below?)
Rovin' tho' his death fell, he went wi' heart at ease,
An' dreamin' arl the time o' Plymouth Hoe.

'Take my drum to England, hang et by the shore,
Strike et when your powder's runnin' low;
If the Dons sight Devon, I'll quit the port o' Heaven,
An' drum them up the Channel as we drumm'd them long ago.'

Drake he's in his hammock till the great Armadas come,
(Capten, art tha sleepin' there below?)
Slung atween the round shot, listenin' for the drum,
An' dreamin' arl the time o' Plymouth Hoe.

Call him on the deep sea, call him up the Sound,
Call him when you sail to meet the foe;
Where the old trade's plyin' an' the old flag vlyin'
They shalt find him ware an' wakin',
as they found him long ago!

Having spent a certain amount of my Naval career in and around HMS *Drake* and being familiar with the love/hate relationship (love to take your money, hate for you to stay around and enjoy it) that every Base Port has with the 'Royal Corps of Naval Sailors' (as Jack occasionally styles himself), I wrote this parody, with apologies to J. Arthur himself, as a tongue-in-cheek observation of the nightly goings-on in and around Plymouth's Union Street. *BB*

RANK'S GONG

Bernie Bruen

J. Arthur's in the foyer, not a pair of miles away.
(Can I have a choc ice and a cone?)
In between the station and the docks around Millbay
Somewhere down the town from Plymouth Hoe.
Yonder lies the dockyard and out from all the ships
The matelots come to dance and see the show,
With the strobe-lights flashing
and the 'fast black taxi' dashing,
He's seen it all develop as he planned it long ago.

Now, Rank he warn't no Devon man, nor spoke no Devonese;
(Can I have a choc ice and a cone?)
But he took a run-down fleapit on a ninety nine year lease,
Somewhere down the town from Plymouth Hoe.
'Take my Gong to England. Put it on the screen.
'Strike it at the start of every show.
'If the films quit Devon, you can close it down, by heaven;
'Convert it to a dance hall; charge 'em twice as much to go.'

Now, Arthur's in the foyer, for the music's rather strong;
(Can I have a choc ice and a cone?)
Stood between the bouncers, listening for the gong,
Somewhere down the town from Plymouth Hoe.
Call him from the dance floor. Call him from the band.
Tell him when the scene is getting slow.
When the drinks are plying and the shirt tails flying,
You can hear him and his 'heavies' saying,
'Right Jack, out you go'
(But I only wanted a choc ice!)

❖ ❖ ❖

HMS *Ganges* and HMS *St Vincent* (were training establishments for boy entrants 15/16 years). Each year at Christmastime, just before the Autumn Term broke up and trainees escaped for a well-deserved break with their families, concerts were usually held at which the Training Staff would perform for the benefit of the trainees, rather than the other way round, which was the norm during term time. It was all 'tongue in cheek' stuff. The song below was sung by the Physical Training Staff at the 1965 concert at HMS *St Vincent* (of which I was part), sung to the tune of 'Camp Grenada'. *Dickie Barr*

'LEST YOU FORGET'

We teach you climbing, teach you vaulting,
We teach you marching, teach you halting,
And when you're falling then we catch you,
Just like mother hens except we do not hatch you.

We teach you rugby, teach you swimming,
We teach you football and ways of winning,
When you're losing to your peers,
Just come to us, we'll wipe away your tears.

We teach you bowling, teach you running,
We teach you softball, teach you cunning,
If you're caught upon some cheating,
Then tell us and we'll hold a friendly meeting.

We teach you diving, teach you jumping,
And ways of box and, avoid a thumping,
We teach you blocking, teach you stopping,
We'll do everything except your dirty washing.

We teach you hockey, teach you sailing,
We teach you rowing and ways of bailing,

When you capsize, please be brave,
We'll be with you, coz our job is your life to save.

Your muscles aching, your backs a-breaking,
Your blisters weeping, your will a-weakening,
Just when you think things can't get worse,
We will happily become your personal nurse.

We teach you fencing, and water polo
We teach you Judo, on the Do-Jo
So when you leave here, being drafted,
Don't forget us men from whom your skills were crafted

Wherever RN ratings met their American counterparts, in bars, taverns or clubs around the world, Jolly Jack could be relied upon to express his feelings towards his allied compatriots through boisterous song. What followed was always predictable. There were many different versions of this particular song, but this is the one I remember best of all. It was sung to the tune, 'Halls of Montezuma'. *Dickie Barr*

There's a buzz going round the harbour
That the Yanks are going to sea
With gallons of Pepsi Cola
And freezers full of ice cream
They look natty when at anchor
Or tied up to the quay
They are bloody good kids in harbour
But Oh by Christ at sea!

THE BLACK RUBBER BAND

Thanks to Nick Gawthrop for this contribution.
We understand that he wrote it when on course
at 'Whaley' (HMS EXCELLENT, Whale Island)

Tune: The Black Velvet Band

In a neat little place they call Whaley
Apprentice a-trade I was bound
And many's the hours sweet doubling
I spent on that great parade ground;
But a sad misfortune came over me,
Which caused me to stray from the Island,
Far away from the bull and Divisions,
Betrayed by the black rubber band.

I took a stroll to the Causway
Not meaning but long for to stray,
When who should I spy but a Chief GI
Come marching along the highway.
He was both bold and salty,
His brightwork it shone in the sun
And his shadow hung over the Island
And SHOUTED at everyone.

I chopped a salute to this ugly old brute
And I smiled as I passed him by
But I knew that he meant the ruin of me
By the look in his rheumy red eye.
He noticed my scruffy old uniform
And the webbing I held in my hand
And he said, "You are scruffy and idle.
Get doubling around the Island."

"I've doubled around your parade ground,"
I told this GI with a sneer,
"And, although I've got views on your parentage,
I've taken it all in good cheer.
But this is too much and I'm telling you
You're gonna get more than you planned."
And with that I pulled out my pusser's dirk
And cut off his black rubber band.

Upon Commander's Defaulters
Next morning I had to appear.
The Commander, he said with a voice like ice,

*"You're case it is proven clear.
It's certain a gunner you never shall be
So I'll send you away from the Island
To be GDO Blind of a PAS boat*
Betrayed by a black rubber band."*

Chorus:

*His boots they shone like diamonds.
I thought him the Chief of the land
And his trousers hung over his gaiters
Held up with a black rubber band.*

*GDO Blind – Gun Direction Officer (Radar)
*PAS boat – Dockyard stores vessel

MIASQ at the Coxn's Cabin, Marsascala, Malta, Bernie Bruen presenting the photo of the band to its proprietor.

Some of the crew of HMS *Gavinton* in formal pose.

Clearance Divers having completing another 'Horsea Island Mud Run'.

The distinguished 'Rusty B' – HMS *Bulwark* – in her commando carrier role
shortly before being sent to the breakers.

Type 14 Frigate HMS *Hardy* executing a turn to starboard in the North Sea.

Paddle tug *Griper* in the Firth of Forth, a type of tug specially designed to manoeuvre aircraft carriers in, out and around harbours.

Minehunter HMS *Gavinton*; over 70 of her class were commissioned in the RN.

'*Toadfish*' – a Wessex 4 helicopter landing on HMS *Albion*.

Bernie Bruen (left) and Richard Barr aboard HMS *Bulwark*, 1975.

Billy Seymour and Fiddler Jim Jennings.

Bernie Bruen defusing an Argentinian mine during the Falklands War, 1982.

9.   Solomon Grundy Inc.

A good number of expatriate Brits and Loan Service RN have served in the Sultan of Oman's Navy, and indeed still do. At the beginning of the first Gulf War, they were a close knit and happy company and, before the days of widespread videos, entertained themselves with song and music. The band 'Solomon Grundy' was made up of a loose group of officers who produced the basis for these entertainments. The name arose because someone said that they:

> *'Got together on a Monday.*
> *Rehearsed on Tuesday.*
> *Played on Wednesday.*
> *Died on Thursday.'*

However, for a good few years Solomon Grundy Inc did sterling entertainment service and invented a few new cocktails to boot. These became known as 'Solomon Grundy Inc Drinks'.

Here's the first of them:

SLEEPING SICKNESS

(A Solomon Grundy Inc Drink)

Take and mix together the following:
½ carton of Pineapple juice
¼ carton of Orange juice
½ can of Coconut milk (or the fresh stuff, if you can get it)
Between ¼ to ½ bottle of the blackest Rum (to taste)
Just the right amount of Grenadine
A grating of Nutmeg (most important) and some ice.

'Shakeitup – Drinkitdown – Sleepitoff!'

THE SHOLTO SHARPNAH

(A Solomon Grundy Inc Drink)

Take one tot of Cointreau,
add a tot of Blue Curacao and a glass of dry white wine.
Add nine drops of Angostura Bitters
and splash in soda to taste.

'This is a very Fine Libation.'

MAJOR TOM

(A Solomon Grundy Inc Drink)

Take a long glass and enter into it one tot of Malibu,
a similar of Appleton's rum,
one measure of Cointreau and top up with ginger ale.

'It's great!' – Bar-Opinion Weekly

THE BLUE DRINK – 'Antifreeze'

(A Solomon Grundy Inc Drink)

1 bottle of champagne
1 bottle of Merrydown cider
4 tots of Grand Marnier
1 tot of Blue Curacao

'A strong fizzy coolant'

THE PINK DRINK – 'In the Pink'

(A Solomom Grundy Inc Drink)

1 bottle of champagne
1 bottle of Mateus Rosé
3 tots of Cointreau

A Solomon Grundy Inc drink Warning!

Do not try the Solomon Grundy Inc drink, '**NAPOLEON'S RETREAT** (Brandy, Vodka & Stones Ginger Wine) – *it's lethal!*

'DRAGONS BREATH'

(A Solomon Grundy Inc drink)

Tomato juice,
a glass of medium sherry,
one teaspoonful of Tabasco,
one tablespoonful of Worcestershire sauce, salt and pepper.

'A great drink for the lunchtime after the night before'.

HMS GLAMORGAN ON THE ROCKS – 30.11.81

(A Solomon Grundy Inc Drink)

1 tot of Bols Kummel
1 tot of Dubonnet
1 tot of Pusser's rum
1/2 bottle of lemonade and rocks (ice)

(Concocted in honour of the sad event, which occurred despite warnings, which could have prevented the incident.)

10. Overheard in the Mess

Enter any mess on any ship, or, in any shore establishment in the Royal Navy and you will hear Naval Officers and Ratings banter among themselves in a language that, more than often, only they would understand. It would require wonderful memories to record here all those quotes and ditties that the authors heard in their careers. However, here are some that are safe to be included in a book for public consumption.

Conversation in the wardroom over breakfast, concerning Harrier Aircraft:
　　"Of course, you have to find specially shaped people to fly them."
　　"Yeah! Pilots."
　　Anon

Two officers discussing the merits of different boats over dinner:
　　'The perfect boat is the one you've already got.'
　　Anon

An 'oppo' leaving HMS Victorious for 'civvy street' tells his messmates;
　　"I've got myself a Job For Life."
　　"Where?"
　　"In a funeral parlour"!
　　Barr

*RB addressing the new intake of Midshipmen joining his mess
for sea training in HMS Eastbourne 1966*

"Now listen up all of you Sir's. The only 'ism' I will permit
during your time in this mess, is vulgarism!"

Barr

Conversation heard in the video library queue:

'Why are you in Blues? We are in Yellow. You are supposed to
be in Whites.'

'Oh, I thought we were still in Orange.' *(and)*

'We are in Yellow, aren't we?'

'No, that's the Army. We are in Amber.'

'How long will we be in that?'

'Oh, ages and ages, I should think.'

'Does that mean we shall be "Forever Amber"?'

Oman 10.12.90

*Of a certain messmate who, when on a run ashore always
jumped up and excused himself to go to the heads when it was
his turn to pay for a round of drinks:*

Daisy Edwards there, don't you think? Does a fair impression
of the 'Cornish Wallet Dance' when the glasses are nearly
empty'

Barr

*Jock McConachy: On the Junior Ratings mess acquiring a TV
for the first time in HMS Rampart. 1960.*

"I think that Fidelity is an excellent 'moral'. Now we can
watch 'Football Highlights' on Saturday nights!"

LH. "Don't you mean 'model', Jock?"

JM. "Don't confuse me or I'll fill you in"

Barr

To JL
  'My alarm clock hates me.'
  'Why do you think that?'
  'It keeps waking me up.'
  Bruen

Describing his latest voyage to those in the wardroom:
  "We sailed all day towards the horizon and when we got there, do you know what we found? There was another one – but it was further away. It was all so terribly, terribly exasperating".
  Bruen

Officer discussing his proposed new spectacle purchase over dinner:
  'Someone told me that there is a new opticians in Muscat, but I've never seen it.'
  JL

Of a chicken masala that turned out to be a vegetable masala:
  'Steward! This is chickenlessnessful!'
  Anon

At breakfast in the wardroom:
  "Gerry, put that Lee and Perrins down and listen to the conversation."
  Gerry. I'd rather read the label."
  Bruen

RB to a Midshipman upon joining his mess, HMS EASTBOURNE 1967: "Don't forget, the only safe pleasure for Midshipmen aboard this ship is a packet of Liquorice Allsorts!"

Barr

Senior Officer to Junior Officer at noisy Mess dinner:
'We are not noisy at THIS end of the table'
'No Sir, but you are all so senior that you HAVE to be quiet.'
Bruen

Heard in the wardroom!
Verbal assurances from your Appointer are not worth the paper they are written on.

Anon

Half a conversation overheard:
'Coz we are all human – well, most of us – except Bernie. He's a robot.'
'Yes, but they haven't finished building him yet.'
Anon

RB 'giving it wellie' in the midships Seamen's Mess, HMS Mull Of Galloway 1961:
"I tell you now that honesty is not a useful quality for advancement in the Navy. PO 'Tug Wilson' told his Captain in Ark Royal that he might possibly have, but couldn't remember, throwing a beer bottle at me when I was a member of the shore patrol called to the incident in the Squizo Bar in Gib – and he got busted down to Leading Hand for it". *Barr*

During 'drinks' in the Senior Rates' Mess. Engineer to Captain:

"I did not like to tell you before, Sir, but your cabin is the only space in the ship that is not air-conditioned."

"Well, b***** me!"

Petty Officer Stoker: "What? In that heat?"

Anon

The following announcement was greeted with hilarity and a round of applause in the first class restaurant car of The 0940, King's Cross to Edinburgh, 125 train which had problems.

Guard: 'We will be calling at Alexandra Palace to pick up the Emergency Travelling Technician, who has asked to come with us to Peterborough. Please bear with us; we are doing our utmost best but it is not good enough.'

HT at HMS Nelson Mess Dinner:

"They have really buggered this beef up!"

BB, (nicely sucked in): "It's venison, you wally!"

Bruen

Female guest at Ladies' Night:

"Why do you pass the port to the left?'

Royal Navy Captain: "Because I expect to get a decanter back from my starboard beam'

Anon

Land Rover's new vehicle, 'Discovery', being discussed in the wardroom:

JK thought it was a space ship. *MG* thought it was a car. *BB* thought it was a boat and *KM* thought it was a sofa.

Bruen

Senior officer at Mess Dinner to young lieutenant:
  'I hope you are going to behave yourself this evening.'
  'Yes – badly!'
  Anon

At the mess table:
  "Pass me the milk!" "
  "Then use the magic word."
  "Sorry. Pass the F**king milk."
  "Thank you."
  Bruen

Conversation between 'seagull-like' Naval Officer's wife and ex Sherwood Forester, JN, at party in Combined Service Officers' Mess.
  'My husband's a Commander!' (which he wasn't)
  JN 'So, what about him?'
  'Well, he's very keen on yachting and wants me to make him a burgee. But where do I get a flag?
  JN: 'If he is in the Navy – no problem. They've got lots of flags.
  'Yes, but where do I get one?'
  JN: "Well, 'X' is in Training. He'll give you one.'
  'Oh no! Dreadful man; we do not talk to that sort of person.'
  JN: 'He happens to be a very good friend of mine.'
  Then, to the assembled company: 'Any man who interferes with this woman is too idle to masturbate!'
  Anon

Captain TB, RM, Bulwark Med deployment, 1975:

'I have worked out that, during this deployment, if I spend eighteen hours per day in my "pit" we shall only be away from UK for two weeks.'

Bruen

Conversation in the wardroom of a square-rigged Tall-ship, in fog, in the Dover Straits, July 1996. Bos'n:

"Here we are, under full sail in the most dangerous waters in the world; visibility's down to half a mile; the Captain's permanently on the radar and the Supply Officer has the watch.. Yet all the key people in the ship are here in the wardroom eating strawberries."

Navigator, "So, what should we do about it?"

Sailing Master, "Have another strawberry."

Bruen

Conversation in the sparsely inhabited TV room, Senior Rates Mess, HMS DRAKE, 1974, while watching the ballet Swan Lake.

Chief GI "Why are half of the female dancers wearing black frocks and the other half white ones?"

Chief PTI. "They are not dancers, they are ballerinas, they are not frocks, they are tutus' and it's so that it can be shown in Africa without upsetting the natives, now shut up, watch and learn"

Chief Cook "That's a load of crap. It's so that you can tell the goodies from the baddies "

PO.Cook, after a pause "That male swan hovering at the back of the stage looks more like a vulture than a swan to me!"

Chief GI "That can't be a swan. What is a male swan called anyway?"

PO. Cook "A vulture."

Chief GI "Then what are female swans called?"

Chief Cook "Geese"

Chief PTI jumping up and switching channels, "You lot are the dregs, no culture, no knowledge and no f..king idea!

The assembled crowd as the Chief PTI storms out: "Good, now we can watch Magic Roundabout"

Barr

AS to BB at breakfast:

"You did not sleep well last night?"

"How do you know?"

"Your face is the wrong shape."

Bruen

Discussion on the decline of the Navy in the Chief's Mess HMS Bulwark 1975:

Chief PTI: "The Navy lost its appeal to me when they stopped the tot in 1967.

Chief Electrician: "No. Decadence really set in when they issued sailors with army style berets. They look like hot water bottles on sailors heads."

Chief Steward: "It'll get a whole lot worse when they allow women to serve at sea!"

Barr

BB, eating a plate of sausage and mash:

"These bangers are not much good."

JH, "Yeah, they only go pop".

Bruen

In the Stewards mess, trying encourage them to enter a team in the ship's KO competition, HMS Victorious, 1964:

"Listen Guys! Playing football is like shagging! You should do it, not talk about it!"

Barr

Heard in the forward seamen's mess, HMS Solebay,1958.

"Sling the slide along Chuck. Cheers!"

(Pass the margarine, Able Seaman Berry. Thanks.)

Barr

Heard at a Midshipmen's briefing, HMS Eastbourne 1966:

The following phrases may help you in future to avoid a Court Martial:

"Cover for me oppo".

"Great idea Sir" and

"It was like that when I took over."

Barr

Overheard in the Chief's mess, HMS Bulwark, on the subject of computers;

'The greatest thing since they re-invented unsliced bread.

Anon

Senior Rates mess, HMS St Angelo, 1972:

LP *(of his Maltese wife):* "When she's angry she speaks 10 different languages.

RB. Well, what's the problem with that?

LP. I don't understand any of them."

Barr

Duty Messman to Chief Stoker in HMS Finistere

"I hear we are off to Brazil next. You know... The place where the nuts come from."

Barr

Home early

"You went home early last night."

"Well, I was talking with 'X' and after a bit one just HAS to go home."

"Oh, I did not realise that there WAS a raffle last night."

Bruen

Sweet truth

"You're not having sugar, are you?"

"Why not?"

"Well, it's Lent"

"But you're having sugar."

"Ah yes, but I'm not religious."

"So, how do you know it's Lent?"

"Instinct!"

Anon

Royal Marines officer describing a punk rocker on TV:

"It looked as though he had just plugged himself into the national grid."

Anon

A good start

"The best breakfast is steak, two eggs and a glass of Guinness."

JMB

Highlights from 1985 Football Cup Final commentary over the ships SRE:

'Frank Stapleton's got a little head on.'

'The trainer is going on to offer himself.'

'Gary Baily – punching not too competitively.'

'Hughes finds Robinson with his stockings round his ankles.'

'He took aim like a telescopic rifle.'

'Gidman, happy to stand on the ball.'

'He snaps up the ball like a yellow biscuit.'

'The Everton supporters like a sea of stone; no noise, no movement, only colour.'

He's.. running down the line like a red and white lighthouse.'

and,

'it bounced off the post! If the post hadn't been there – it would have gone in.'

Anon

Heard in a wardroom mess discussion:

"The difference between capitalism and communism is that with capitalism, man exploits man. With communism it is the other way round."

Anon

Off days

"It seems that today is yet another bank holiday – again."

"Really, I don't understand what is happening to this country."

"Oh, I like it. If we are going to go down, we might as well go down in a holiday spirit."

Anon

Heard on Children's Television in January 1986:

'George's Grandma was a wizened old woman, with pale brown teeth and a small, puckered-up mouth like a dog's bottom.'

Anon

Upon seeing what was in the tray for dinner in HMS Solebay, an AB stated:

'We Scots eat our Oats. The Welsh eat their Rarebit. The Irish eat their Stew while the heathen English, eat these Scabby Babies Heads!' (*Suet Puddings*).

Barr

Eccentric and elderly doctor of Royal Fleet Auxiliary, accompanying HMS Bulwark across the Atlantic, comes out of his reverie at dinner:

'They're building bridges that fall down!'

Anon

Over the ships tannoy system:

'D'y' hear there! Anyone knowing the whereabouts of the Captain's Table, report to the bridge now!'

Bruen

Grubby garment

"That's the fifth time you've worn that T-shirt at breakfast."

"Well, it's my breakfast T-shirt."

"Yes, but it should be printed on – not actually there."

Anon

During the ships visit to Calais where French sailors were entertained in our mess, the Leading Hand remarked loudly:

In my book, you French are perfectly entitled to exist, eat frogs legs, snails and be merry – as long as you do it in France.

Barr

After inadvertently dropping his false teeth into the filled mess tea urn, BBA told the young Ordinary Seaman who saw it happen:

If word of this leaks out, I will throw you over the side!

Barr

RB to Pilot Officer SB, on showing her the hole he had just burned in the front of her ball gown with a travel iron. Officer's Mess RAF Mountbatten, 1995:

'Would you like me to drive home and fetch another one Ma'am, or will I dismiss myself while the going's good?"

Barr

BB and GH discussing the Royal Navy:

'I believe in what Churchill said, "Sodomy and the Lash".'

'Oh, you're teetotal are you?'

Bruen

Mess discussion on marriage:

Women do have at least one positive thing going for them. They don't have to marry one.

Barr

11.   OBITA DICTA

Incidental remarks (from the Latin *obiter* 'by the way' and *dicta* 'things said') a collection gathered over the years by Bernie Bruen and Richard Barr.

> *He wondered if he really believed what he was saying or if he was speaking for the instruction of the young – who were not listening.*
>
> *John Masters – 'Now God be Thanked'*

A sailors response to service in submarines ceasing to be voluntary only.

'I feel about submarines the way I feel about package holidays. They are OK for others to go in.'

Barr

Discussing his overweight condition:

'I have often tried to examine my motives. The biggest problem I have is finding them.'

DS

A 'Vice' Admiral is a senior officer who enjoys a smoke or two, a gin or two, a young lady or two and possibly sodomy. But not necessarily in that order!

Barr

'In old age it is better to contemplate failure than success.'

Anon

A copy of Fiddler Jenning's tape recording 'To Air is Humane' is passed on, as the Arabian evening condensation forms upon the cover, 'Ah, the Air is Humid!'

"Richard Son! One needs a great constitution with which to grow old! *My mother, Connie, aged 94, 2010*
    Barr

RB's lame response to Chief GI after dropping his rifle on the parade ground in HMS RALEIGH 1958.
    Chief GI "Stand still there you ugly little shite! Now then, tell me. Is there a history of insanity in your family?"
    RB: I think so Chief GI, my dad suggested that I should join the Navy.
    Barr

During breathing apparatus training at HMS PHEONIX, leading up to the National Firemen's Strike. 1978
    Using CS Gas, In some trainees eyes – is wrong.
    Barr

'Seasickness'.
    In the beginning you think you are going to die, then you hope you are going to die; finally, and worst of all, you realise that you are not going to die. After that you start to get better.
    Colin Jarman, 'Coastwise and Beyond'

RB to Jethro 1995
    My new song starts off at a cracking pace, then settles into a steady canter and finally, it just peters out.
    Barr

Hindsight

"The first ten years of my life were poor. The second ten were worse. The third ten were horrible, then things went rapidly downhill!"

Barr

Lt Cdr M, on learning that the newly-arrived Commander of HMS VERNON had been promoted:

'That's always happening here. The place is like a lay-apart store.'

Anon

About EB, on Snowdon 1978

I'd rather have him in the tent puking out, than outside puking in.

Barr

Chaplehay pub in Weymouth, closing time. PO Diver G sits with half a pint of Guinness in front of him.

Landlady, indicating glass: 'One swallow?'

PO Diver looking at glass: 'Does not a summer make.'

Anon

New arrival

His wife had a baby last week. I should have thought it the kind of thing that would, rather spoil one's leave; but he seems quite cheerful.

Apthorpe

Of Commander Laughton, 1975

Modest! Good God no. He had a passion for destroying his fellow officers. *Barr*

Signal from HMS ALBION to Greek Destroyer that had completely disappeared from bridge view when cutting close across her bows:

'That was unseamanlike.'

Captain Henry Leach

HMS TERROR 1963

'Scotch Broth' The contents of a matelots stomach found in the back of a Singapore taxi after a night on Vat 69.

Barr

Three Weeks in the Appalachian Mountains Without Food – by Steven Morris

Day One – Felt pretty weak by mid-afternoon.

Day Seventeen – Can no longer write.

SM

American pilot on exchange to HMS VICTORIOUS, 1963

'Clubs!' Playing rugby is such goddam fun. You can get away with things that in any other circumstances they would put you in jail for!

Barr

> *Beware the lurking Postal Strike,*
> *That nasty, evil, skulking tyke,*
> *Who, from its lair, comes out at night*
> *To creep close to us from behind*
> *And, when it's fawned and cowered and whined,*
> *Will sneak, malicious, scratch and bite.*
>
> *Bruen, 7th Sept 88*

Better to have Enemies than Friends; Enemies don't let you down.

Bruen

Captain to First Lieutenant in Norwegian Fjord, HMS RAMPART, 1960:

"You call. Heads we take the Port passage, tails we take the Starboard."

Barr

'I would not ask you to lie; you have not had the proper diplomatic   training.'

Film 'Sea Chase'

Pipe heard aboard USS SARATOGA in Yokohama

"Liberty guys to glamorize, muster abaft the after smoke-stack.

Barr

Divisional Officer to RB & JP at bi-annual review, HMS COLLINGWOOD, 1968:

"I am going to award you eleven good conduct points, now go away and share them between you!"

Barr

First Lieutenant to Captain, that the Lower Deck has been cleared:

'Your ship's company is mustered, Sir.'

'Mustard? Yes, I know they are.'

Bruen

Coxswain to RB after yet another appearance at Captain's defaulters, HMS RAMPART, 1961.

"If you continue to go through life with your head buried in the sand, all people will ever see of you is your arse!

Barr

In London they are selling paper and bamboo Chinese umbrellas called 'one shower brollies'. ('Wanchi Burburries' -- You work it out.)

Anon

I am fair-minded, unbiased and lacking in prejudice – what woman could say that?

Bruen

RB to Divisional Officer. HMS ST ANGELO 1972

"I have a theory sir, I believe that everybody's heart has the same number of beats programmed into them and that's why the lazy live the longest. I have used 75% of my allocation already and I'm only 25 years old. I am going to take it easy from now on so don't expect too much of me."

Barr

'What's Rickie's surname?' 'Rickie who?'

Anon

'It is not fair!'
'What is your basis for comparison?'

Bowie

I try to explain clearly what I mean, but words always get in the way. *Barr*

Bruen on training support

Give me Earth, Water and Straw; I will make you Bricks with which you may build a Monument. Withhold the Straw and the Bricks will soon crumble. Deny me the Water and all that is left will blow away. As Dust in the Wind.

Royal Marine's view of the Falklands Islands in 1983:

'It's rather like covering yourself in a bucket of diesel and standing in front of a brick wall for a couple of hours.

JM

Of women being allowed to go to sea in ships;

Women these days don't find it difficult to behave like men. They just do it with less conviction.

Barr

We all have something to offer – the problem is finding a worthy recipient.

Bruen

Grab a chance and you won't be sorry for a might-have-been. (and) let Enjoyment, not Endurance be your Watchword.

Arthur Ransome, 'We Didn't Mean to go to Sea'

All that one needs is the will to voyage and a good ship under-foot. *Anon*

It looked like a valid test in the world of quick-and-dirty boat building, and the exploding-skiff theory receded in favour of newer and more exciting dilemmas.
Bill Schwicker, 'A Three Fathom Sharpie'

Chief Instructor of Rally Driving School, after car returns from student aptitude test:
'A hundred and ten miles an hour across THAT terrain?!!'
Student: 'Well, she'll do a hundred and ten so I did a hundred and ten.'

RB, upon being asked what he would prefer doing during an enforced 'leave cancellation' HMS BULWARK, Malta 1974.
The things I really like doing are either illegal, immoral or out of bounds. *Barr*

What do Baghdad and Hiroshima have in common? Nothing – yet! *SM*

I would be apathetic, but I can't be bothered; lethargic – but I'm too tired. *Bruen*

To class of Junior Stokers in HMS ST VINCENT, 1965
'If God had wanted junior stokers to bend over, he would have stationed priests behind them.
Barr

There were four types of people taking part:
Those few who knew what they were doing.

Those who thought they knew what they were doing but did not.

Those who had no idea of what they were doing, and

Those who had no idea of what they were doing but told everyone that they had.

These last were in charge.

Koetef

From an Italian News report, 28.1.91:

Eleven Omani warships are fighting in the Iraq War. Twelve more are moving to their assistance. (Note: Oman only had a dozen warships and most of those were in harbour at the time.)

Christmas comes but once a year; tiz your duty to keep clear.

Bruen

'*NUCLEAR SUBMARINE SWALLOWED BY GIANT WHALE!*'

The story behind this headline has yet to turn up but Hollywood is working on it.

Barr

RH: The gods are with us.

BB: Inshallah

Bruen

Every man needs a shed.

JS on BB

Marriage is a compromise. Life is a compromise. Lucky and rare is he who is not subject to such things.

Bruen

We must strive to be unsuccessfulnesslessful.
Lt Brammel, USN

RB to new recruit tying the laces of his gym shoes. HMS ST VINCENT 1965:
"Don't bend over in front of me sonny. Who do you think I am. A vicar?" *Barr*

BB: 'What do you do with all these poems I give you?'
SM: 'They all go in a big file labelled "chicken-shit".'
Bruen

Men must always be making traps for men, or they are not content. *Mowgli*

Upon receiving a bollocking from HMS RAMPART's Captain for serving up another 'under par' supper 1960
"My mother and father are Irish Sir! I am entitled to be mis-understood"
Barr

JH (who is dyslexic), 'I have difficulty reading the subtitles at the movies – especially if they are in Chinese.'
JH

'I'm not afraid of heights – just widths.'
SM

Trust no-one – for they cannot trust themselves.
Bruen

'Home is only a destination. Life is at Sea'.
Stephen Sheppard

RB's report to Chief PTI upon discovering masturbating taking place in the swimming pool, HMS ST VINCENT, 1965.

"Chief! I found two dirty little Junior Stokers spawning in the pool just now".

Chief's response: "Then you had better reel the little toads and the evidence into my office!"

Barr

Let the Poet look into his own heart and write but, being wary of sentimentality, let him use his mind fearlessly and to the utmost.

Stillman

Gunnery Instructors on Whale Island Parade Ground:

Chinese chefs screaming Sweet and Sour ingredients at each other.

Barr

I lounged with a passion in all the right places.

JH

Greenwich Mean Time – the incorrect time in London.

Anon

The establishment's dog gives birth to six pups in a flower bed under Training Officer's window, hard by the Parade Ground. *Training Officer to Parade Officer:* 'And why was not the dog on parade with her pups?'
Parade Officer, 'They were only watching. They're New Entry.'

Bruen

Of the Coxswain of HMS RAMPART, upon his escorting a young lady on a tour of the ship, 1960:

'He combines the manners of his rank with the morals of a brothel keeper.'

Barr

It was not only lives that were lost in the Great War, but simplicity, certainty and faith.

Martin Stephen, 'Never Such Innocence'

"I can imagine an American Naval officer returning from Greenwich Naval College and declaring that he had had a 'Real Mean Time'!"

GH

SW, having been shown CMcN's extra-tightly wound and therefore 'miniature' trumpet,

'You must be a Secret Agent for the Salvation Army. Where's your shoulder-holster?' *Bruen*

Any rating that hates marching and sentry duty can't be all that bad! *Barr*

BB to JH: 'Not very quick today, are you?'
'I'm tired after reading your book.'

JH to BB: 'I suppose that is archetypal of the modern ethos.'
'I do not even know what 'ethos' are.'
'Joi-de-veuve... vilv... viver... FUN!'

JH

RA on old Radios and difficulties in tuning them to current broadcasts:

'Mind you, it is still possible to get the Home Service and the Light Programme.'

A River Mersey Pilot: A man who has steered his way through a few tugboats in his time!

Barr

"I think I enjoy showing that it is not necessary to accept, as most people do, the way of life that is expected of them on account of their background and education. If you want to do something different, you can.

Naomi James in 'The Southern Ocean'

There are people in their thirties who do not know when either of the World Wars were fought. They were not taught it at school and think it does not concern them, that it is just 'history'. To forget is the privilege of peace, but it is a luxury that was hard won for them in war.

Bruen

Senior Officer, on departing 'Old Middle East Hand',

'He left behind him a treasure of pure gold – we were, all of us, his students.'

BB: 'When are you going to start writing your book?
RA: 'Not yet a while. I am too busy living it.'

Bruen

RB 'I hate that car'
BB 'I love it'

SB 'I want a red one'
　Bruen

Couple, kissing heavily,
She, 'What are we doing?'
He, 'I hope it's foreplay'.
　Anon

Is the collective noun for 10,000 headmasters, a 'Lakh of Principles'?
　Barr

"There is no such word as *can't*" (and) "Only servants whisper."
　Two gems from MR-M's Nanny

'I'm fed-up with being a shrinking violet.'
'Is that some kind of pansy?'
　Bruen

Two of the most oft used questions:
　'Do you still love me?' and 'When are you going to grow up?'
　Just ignore them.
　Bruen

You don't have to be a good actor to join the 'Victory Players'! You just have to ensure that you don't get a draft chit before the end of the play!
　Barr

Qualified!
　Seen it. Done it. Read the book. Watched the film. Own the video. Passed the course. Written the synopsis. Collected the

picture cards. Completed the jig-saw. Bought the T-shirt. Displayed the sticker. Ticked the box. Got the picture.

> Bruen

Collective nouns:
  Churchmen: A Forest of Deans
  Chinese Dogs: A Fit of Pekes
  Intellectuals travelling by rail: A Train of Thought
  Bruen/Barr

I'll tell you a tale, a sad little tale,
The cautionary tale of Jim.
He cared for nobody. No not he,
And nobody cared for him!

> *JMB*

Would pedestrians grouped at a Pelican crossing be collectively described as 'A Stopper Knot'?

> Bruen

Apart from the fact that all moments in time are unparalleled, the following ranks as the only unique occasion in history:
  One and half-a-score of seconds into the forty-ninth minute before midday on the fourth day of the second week in the penultimate month, eight years before the end of the second decade after the first century of the second millennium.

> Bruen

RNSPT Portsmouth. 1962
"Class, three times round the gym, GO!"
  And to the Chief Staff Instructor, ten minutes after his class had disappeared from sight...

"Staff, I only meant the *inside* of the gym!"
Barr

Significance lies, not in the error of ones ways, but in the ways
of one's error.
Bruen

First Lieutenant: "I'm depressed."
Fellow Officer: Then we are all depressed.
First Lieutenant: Really?
Fellow Officer: No!
JMB

If American films and television are anything to go by, their
male population appear either very insecure or, otherwise,
incestuous. They keep calling each other 'motherf**kers! (I told
my mum to be home before dark if she saw any around).
Barr

The Americans live in America. The Romans live in Rome. The
Germans live in Germany. But the Englishman lives 'at home'.
Anon

'By his ropes shall ye know the true measure of the sailor.'
Frayed ropes ends are cursed and an abomination, but no more
so than an improperly made whipping, for that indicates either
ignorance or indifference. Ignorance is excusable and often
temporary but indifference generally becomes a bad habit.
Harvey Garrett-Smith in 'The Marlinspike Sailor'

A ship is safe in harbour but belongs at sea.
Lieutenant the Prince Shihab bin Tariq bin Taimur al Said of Oman

There is nothing, absolutely nothing, quite half as worthwhile as simply messing about in boats.
Ratty – The Wind in the Willows

Any impulsive proclivity for waving a protest flag will be considered to be a peevish display of nautical impropriety.
Wianno 'Senior' Yacht Club, Nantucket Sound 1914

We are the music-makers:
And are the dreamers of dreams;
Wandering by the lone sea-breakers
And sitting by desolate streams;
World-losers and world forsakers
On whom the pale moon gleams:
Yet we are the movers and the shakers
Of the world for ever, it seems.
A O'Shaughnessy

And its westward-ho for Chideock,
for Titchbourne and Carhaiz,
And, Come-about a hundred times a day.
Tacking from Sawaddi,
Sunset all ablaze,
With a head-wind dead against you all the way.
(BB on Drascomb longboats and weekend sailing in Oman)

Removing the centre cushion from the headrest of a Ford Cortina Ghia converts the car into a 'GT'.

PL

Asked to recognize the two Yanks who had duffed up my oppo the previous night:

"I can't tell one Yank from another Sir! They've all got loud mouths, overlarge egos and even larger backsides."
HMS VICTORIOUS, Olongapo, 1963.

Barr

Women – unseamanlike and unnecessary.

JR-J

There is something slipshod about a woman who allows herself to have nineteen children.

SR

You cannot be a musician and have a girlfriend.

LW

HP's remark to RB prior to BB's epic bout with NC at the 1978 Navy Boxing Championships:

I would not cross the road to get in the ring with Nicky Croombes, much less bike it from Scotland to Portsmouth in eight hours for the pleasure!

Knife-fighting: a satisfying way of expressing feelings to a man you don't much like.

Buddy

BB: 'I've fallen in love?'
RB: 'What "cc"?'
   Bruen

'Bernie, may I have a look at your fiddle?'
'Certainly, it has quite a nice tone actually.'
'Really? I thought it was made of slate.'
   Anon

'No, Dear, one really cannot cry at a Hoover attachment.'
   Irene Handel, on her reaction to the film 'ET

Royal Navy diver, describing a Falmouth run-ashore, the town being inundated with Clearance Diving Teams:
   'When I went to the "Grapes" last night I had to "clear my ears" to get in the door.' *Bruen*

Bishop, at Exeter Flotilla Meeting: 'I have a bit of arthritis in my knees – an occupational hazard I suppose really.'
   Anon

The Rule of Two:
   Currency – Sterling and Monopoly
   Hedgehogs – Fast and Frisbee
   Language – English and Gibberish

The Rule of Three:
   Fowl – Cocks, Hens and Kentucky Fried.
   Ships – Battleships, Tugs and Schooners.
   Fish – Sharks, Kippers and Angels.
   Roads – Highways, Byways and No Through.
   Sheep – Flocks, Rugs and Chops.

Ensigns – Red Ensigns, White Ensigns and 'Flags of Convenience'.

2 CVs – Teachers, Protesters and Vegetarians.

Motorcycles – Jap-crap, Foreign Rubbish and 'Elderly British Machines'

Circuses – Billy Smart's, Bertam Mills' and Piccadilly.

Landing – Airports, Airfields and Aerodromes.

Roads (again)– Those for going, those for coming back and those for getting stuck on.

Helicopters – Those flown by professionals, those flown by amateurs and those flown by Prince Andrew.

Insects – Those that stings you, those that bites you and those that sucks your blood.

Flowers – Them as looks nice, them as smells nice and them as you can make wine out of.

Bruen/Barr

Interview with comedian Jerry Lewis:

'Did you ever want to do serious acting? Did you ever want to play Hamlet?'

'No. What I do is tougher!'

JL

Woman, writing to radio programme:

'While watching Top of the Pops on television the other evening, I noticed that he (the pop singer) had his hands in his pockets – and appeared to be peeling an orange.'

Anon

From a song by Billy Fury: 'Things will change deff-in-ate-lee.'

Thargoid – a kind of urban-guerrilla-drongo.
   RR

Chief Diver to a Diver, skulking on the jetty:
'What's wrong with you?'
   'I'm lonely for my mates.'
   'Don't be lonely, Son. Return your ******* gear!'
   SS

Cox'n of Diving Tender, on telephone to Chief Diver:
   'You vandal, that 30ft ladder you cut in three pieces – it's on my Permanent Loan... don't you laugh, you bastard!'

Reprimand to RN diver: 'It's "Aye-aye, Sir", not "Right-on, Boss"!'
   Bruen

The best gin of the day is the one before breakfast.
   JMB

After run-ashore and kebabs, divers return to friend's digs.
   'Sshhh! Don't make a sound. My "Oppo" is on nights.'
   All tiptoe quietly upstairs.
'Hang about, It's 2330, isn't he at work?
   Anon

Women are never to be entirely trusted – not the best of them.
   Sherlock Holmes, 'The Sign of Four'

TV journalist to Admiral:
   'Was Belgrano an immediate threat?

'No'

'Did she ever become an immediate threat?'

'No, because we sank her!'

HMS GAVINTON, in rough weather – Matthew, ch 14, vs 24

'And the boat was many miles from the shore and beaten by the waves for the wind was against them'

HMS KIRKLISTON, Philippians, ch 2, vs 27:

'and he was very sick.'

Bruen

The sole entry in RB's School Report. 1951

"He has many really rather annoying habits, which his parents should be made aware of."

Barr

If you saw an Italian ship in the distance, would it be a Spick on the horizon. *Gavinton's bridge, Taranto, 1984.*

Bruen

The French are a ridiculous people, the Italians incompetent, the Americans neurotic, the Germans romantically savage, the Arabs vicious, the Russians barbaric – and the Dutch make cheese.

Bruen

Television programmes have over the years become so much crap. Today, with advanced technology, you can watch the same crap in 'high definition' for ten times the price.

Barr

Americans enjoy being abused by waiters. It is their only way of judging the quality of the food.

Bruen

Much of the open land of America is attractive. Sadly, it is populated by Americans. But then one could say a similar thing about Greece or Ireland.

Trevanian

He was a fiddler and consequently a rogue.

J. Swift

I could die in America, but live there? Never!

RB

RS, discussing CO's 'polar-bear' rug

'He would have bought it for children – but only to frighten them.'

'He lacked charm to a degree rarely found outside the Principality of Wales'

from 'Play for Today', Radio Four

Comment from 'chummy' ship's first lieutenant after a certain ship had spent an extended time alongside the wall in repair:

I hear you have Cable TV now.'

Bruen

'Nothing in a woman's life can ever compensate for not being born a man.'

Mrs Robert Falcon Scott (of the Antarctic)

He goes through life as though he had a complimentary ticket.
Last of the Summer Wine

Waiter, in restaurant of slow service:
   'I hope you enjoyed your evening.'
   'One does not enjoy evenings here, one survives them.'
   Anon

Impromptu song engendered by first sight of Forth Navigation's computerised, colour Radar:
   The land is green. The sea is blue. Our colour radar's watching you, And it's raining, raining on my chart."
   AH

Interview with famous violinist:
   'How does a Stradivarius compare with the violin you normally play?'
   'Well, it's bigger.'
   Anon

'He went through 'ere like it were a public convenience' and,
   'Its life, son. At your age it may make you laugh but one day it will make you bloody cry.'
   John Mills – 'The Family Way'

Coxswain of HMS RAMPART to RB, 1960:
   "You're the most unable seaman I have ever had the displeasure to serve with!"
   Barr

A Japanese fighting-boat was arrested by the Soviet Navy, who said that she was in an area where fighting was prohibited.'

BBC News 24 .4 .85

'Onward Christian Bonnington' reached the summit of Everest at the age of 50 on the Queen's birthday, 1985. It was his fourth attempt.

Radio Interviewer to Mrs Bonnington: 'Do you think he will give up climbing mountains now? He IS 50!'

Mrs B: 'Oh no, he has a lot of puff left in him yet – but the others may not be as high...'

BBC

Royal Marine, speaking on BBC's 'Raid on Top Malo':

'Being a Marine and not having a war to fight is rather like being a concert pianist and having no one to play your violin to.

RM

TV Commentator about large, over-weight darts player:

'Oh yes! What an athlete this man is!'

Navigator to Ship's Company, about to pass through the Sound of Islay:

'Modified Special Sea Dutymen will be required for the passage through the narrows. Ship's Company are warned that... er... the area... um... is of extreme beauty and... ah... should not be missed.'

SMcQ

A woman's place is in the wrong.

JJS

Sleep is something one indulges in when tired of living.
Barr

"Pronounce these words as I spell them out... A-I-R.
"Air."
"H-A-I-R."
"Hair."
"L-A-I-R."
"Lair."
'Now repeat the three words together.'
'Air Hair Lair.'
'Air, hair lair to you too, welcome to Dartmouth College.'
Bruen

Ectopic – Anomaly of situation.
Ectopia – The best place to be!
Bruen

'It is at times like this that I wish I'd listened to what my mother told me when I was little.'
'Why, what did she say?'
'I don't know. I wasn't listening.'
SMcQ

Ancient Cornishman at Lerrin, discussing the old lime kiln and the fact that they once used to wheel two hundredweight barrows:
'Well o' course them was muscly in those days, they wor. Cider an' fat bacon, see.'

Captain to Midshipman D:

'What are you going to do with that crate of beer you won in the ship's quiz tonight?'

'I can't drink it all now; I've got the middle watch with the navigator!'

They called me 'articulated' the day I passed my (O level) in English Literature. *Barr*

Comedian: 'Anyone here from London?'
Many voices: 'Yes!'
Comedian: 'Oh good. Whereabouts?'
One voice: 'Over here!'
   Jethro's Club

Junior Seaman W, acting as probationary gangway Quarter-master:

'D'y' hear-there! Confectionery and fresh newspapers are now on sale on the Jetty?'

'People never asked me about my music, just how many strings were left on my guitar.'

   Barr

We think too much of promotion, of getting an easy job, too little of the other thing; too little that we are here to serve our country and not ourselves.

   Fleet Surgeon T. T. Jeans RN

Leading Regulator DL, to RB, from the bottom of a monsoon drain, into which he had just fallen. Sembawang Village, 1964
"I should really run you in for being pissed whilst ashore, oppo."
   Barr

Ship's Captain to those around him:
'What do you call a cow at the north pole?'
Cox'n: 'Lost.'
Chief PO: 'An Eskimoo.'
Midshipman: 'Friesian.'
   Bruen

Do mariners and sub-mariners equate to humans and sub humans?
   Bruen

Nothing fascinates a naval officer more than the sight of another naval officer mis-handling his ship.
   Charles Gidley

It seems so tragic that an organisation like the Royal Navy can recruit so many idealistic young men, so much enthusiasm, determination and loyalty, and leave them at the end of their careers with so little.
   Janaway, 'The Raging of the Sea'

A still tongue holds a wise head.
   J. Grondona

When in Rome – live in Plymouth!
   Fiddler Jennings

Customer, pointing to the beer menu above the fireplace in the Swan Hotel, Devonport:
'What are all those figures ... the specific gravity?'
Landlord: 'No, that's the price, you pillock!'

    Bruen

I love arrogance in a woman. It is so amusing to find out that it is their only defence.

    James Mason

Senior RN Captain's answer to any complaint from his men:
'If you do not like the conditions of service – then go outside!'

Thank God for fools – lest there be no fun.

    JJ

Thank God for women – lest there be no whimsy.

    Bruen

Usually I find that women are only on time when they want to make a scene or bring bad news. I do not know which they enjoy most.

    Stewart Grainger

'Typhoon Peggy caused havoc when it swept over the island of Woppity-Wop in the Bahamas. Mrs So-And-So, the Prime Minister has declared a 'state of calamity'.

    BBC News 7.86

Heard on radio Pop Programme:

He has a knack of getting into the small numbers of the charts with records that do not leap out of the radio saying, "Here's a mega-hit".

Women are always hungry. They are fallopian tubes with teeth.
  Peter Sellers.

'Not to know him is to love him.'
  Cary Grant

'Now here's a treat for all Elvis Presley fans – "Delilah" by Tom Jones.'
  SS. AFRS 'The Brit Show', Diego Garcia

As loudly reported by the duty SBA to the queue of sailors outside the sickbay aboard HMS Solebay, the morning after sailing from Karachi, 1959:

"Able Seaman McDaid, the first one in here today, has just been diagnosed as having Happyrash.' (a dose of the pox).
  Barr

When a woman starts complaining, you know she is thoroughly comfortable in her surroundings.
  Peter Sellers

After the Falklands conflict:

I do not mind dying – but to be accused of journalism...!
  Bruen

You can tell an Admiral's getting old when his Turks Heads start going wrong.

Vice Admiral Sir Donald Gibson KGB DSC RN

People miss the best part of the day if they lie to bed.

EJ (farmer)

Up to 21 a woman is protected by law; at 65 by nature. Anywhere in between she is fair game.

Gary Grant

England is put out of the Football World Cup competition by Argentina:

BB 'Well, it's only a game.'

JH 'Cynic!'

BB 'Realist.'

GB 'Prat!'

'He was never a favourite with women; but, thank heaven, I have better things to do than study their peculiarities.'

Sir Hugh Clanroyden, 'Fountainblue' – *J. Buchan*

I find it quite amazing that every time we fly with the RAF they contrive to make it seem as though they have never done it before.

Bruen

Naval officer (schoolie) to similar:

'I am not keen on doing the night shifts; I prefer day shifts.' (Whatever happened to 'watches'?)

Anon

Geneva Convention, Article 356:

Under no circumstances will basket-making or the gathering of willows for any purpose whatever be permitted.

October 1987.

No one in the Navy – not ships, teams, nor other organisation – can have equipment or articles kept on shelf 'H', or above, in Portsmouth Naval Stores because the machine used to get them down is broken – and has been since May.

Anon

Meanwhile, radio presenter D. Jameson broadcasts the following statement: 'Well, Frank (Bruno), if you're listening, you and me's goin' to sort out this Joe Bugner once and for ALL!'

BBC

When they privatise the Armed Forces, you will probably find the Navy supplied with armaments by the 'Deep Throat Depth Charge Company'.

Barr

28.10.87 – Hunnigan/Bacus title fight:
'Yea, that's cricket. You get this sort of thing in boxing.'

Frank Bruno

Rollerskater in Marathon:

'I got arrested for doing 42mph – backwards down Regent Street. Can't see it myself.'

Anon

SB: His wife went berserk when she found out he was using his new car to conduct an affair!

RB: But I thought she was into RAKI, you know, self-control and all that!

SB: Well she is. She 'wracked' his car for him when she found out!

   Stevie Barr

If, when over-worked, you eventually see a light at the end of the tunnel, it will be somebody with a torch bringing you more work.

BB, at Army-Navy boxing match, to Navy coach, about Navy boxer X:

'Have you seen anything of 'X' lately?'

'I see him in Pompey every now and again.'

'Can you understand what he says?'

'Yes, but I don't believe it.'

   Bruen

'I have never been so miserable since I married my wife ... being away from her, I mean.'

   TP

People say to me, 'Go for it!' So I went for it. It had gone.

   Shadwell

Twins, aged five, talking about a naval wedding they had recently attended:

   'Some people did not have any clothes – so they had to wear sailor's clothes.'

   Anon

There are three types of cars: racing cars, invalid carriages and the one that I'm driving.

    Bruen

Overheard at the Holland Inn:
'My boss is on first-name terms with Roger DeSavary'
'You mean PETER DeSavary.'

    Anon

The Hot Dog – the only case of feeding the hand that bites it.

    Anon

'Sebastian Coe's coach said that Coe's best days are behind him and that he would be lucky to make selection for the Seoul Olympics, let alone win a medal.' *BBC News*

'Mrs Seymour, would you judge the Baby Contest?'
'My God! Do they have to fight?'

    'First Among Equals'

Show me a retired naval officer and I'll show you an embittered man.

    Jannaway, 'The Raging of the Sea'

'That's life in a blue shemarg – Sinbad.' *(or 'That's life in a blue suit-Jack')* Anon

You can drive a horse to water but a ball-weight must be lead.

    (Clearance diving saying)

'Faith' is a pusser's Dan-buoy.

    JJS

Heard in Devonport Pub
Abattoir worker: 'The smell that comes out of that pasty factory is disgusting.'
Landlord: 'Well, it is not exactly brilliant out of your place, is it?'
   Anon

To become the hunted, having been the hunter, must be really irksome.
   Bruen

Nothing could be more harmful than to sit a child down at the piano and teach it to hate music.
   Peter Savage, 'Far, Far the Mountain Peak'

'What? What! Now, yes... You... yes... Um.... I'm just sorting my brain.'
   Commander RN on the telephone

Winding up a watch is a waste of time.
   Barr

Butt-end of half a telephone conversation overheard:
   'You think because you have car you are big fellow. You be careful or I throw your body into the sea!'
   Bruen

At a Heads of Department meeting:
   'When will the ex-CO's relief cease to be referred to as "the new CO" and be called "the CO"?'
   'After one week.'
   Anon

'I'm sorry to have to leave the meeting early but I must go to the dentist to have holes drilled in my teeth.'

'Why don't you just send them along in a glass of water?'

Anon

Memorandum from the CO:

'As requested at reference A, the implications of reference B are forwarded at Annex A.'

Anon

"The trouble with words is, you never know who's mouth they've been in."

Dennis Potter

BB 'It all goes to show – God looks after fools and drunks.'
SM. 'I'll drink to that'
Anon. 'You fool'

Bruen

Three 'bon-mots' by MR-M:

"Most naval officers I know regard a ditch as a haven."

"Here's a little story about Veuve Cliquot, which I happen to know is a very good champagne – I was christened in it."

"In our day Wellington College used to produce upper-class wide-boys."

Anon

CMcN: 'Why is the wind-sock at half-mast?'
BB: 'The wind must have died.'

Bruen

Women – you have to admire the way they frighten people and mend vacuum cleaners.

Clegg, Last of the Summer Wine

Carney: 'You got married?'
Niven; Yes, three times.'
Carney: 'Children?'
Niven: 'No, grown women every time.'

Anon

East London street pedlar:

'Lobsters! You want 'em, I got 'em. Fresh lobsters, straight out the sea. They're 'ere. They're lovely. Getcha lobsters...'
Gangland heavy: "Ron 'ere don't like lobsters.'
Trader rips off lobster's claws: 'Crayfish, I got 'em! Getcha crayfish 'ere.'

Anon

If the camel is the ship of the desert, you ought to see my boss. He's like a desert lighthouse – bright but useless.

EJ

A critic is someone who enters the battlefield after the fighting is over and bayonets the wounded.

Anon

A sailor needs a hole in a boat like an orchestra needs bagpipes.

Barr

Eid is a-comin' and the goats are getting worried. They fear they may be eaten, either fried with rice or curried.

CW

The *Daily Mirror* is read by people who think they run the country.

The *Guardian* is read by people who think they ought to run the country.

The *Times* is read by people who actually do run the country.

The *Daily Mail* is read by the wives of the people who run the country.

The *Financial Times* is read by people who own the country.

The *Morning Star* is read by people who think the country should be run by another country.

The *Daily Telegraph* is read by people who think it is.

And *Sun* readers don't care who runs the country as long as she's got big tits.

'Yes Prime Minister'

Englishmen that the French hate most of all are Lord Nelson, The Duke of Wellington, The Duke of Marlborough and Norman Wisdom – all four for bringing tears to their eyes!

Barr

I blame altitude for forgetfulness, not old age. Every time I go aloft for something, I forget what it was I went up for. When I come down again, I remember.

Barr

Life is the predicament that precedes death.

CW

You set a sail and see where it takes you. You make friends, then you move on. All you can do is remember as best you can.

Bruen

SM, 'Abdullah, when you say "wishy-washy", what does it mean?
AS, " It's not quite "iffy!"
   Bruen

You have two eyes, two ears and one mouth. Use them accordingly (unless you are a politician, then just use the mouth).
   Anon

'Where abilty ends – arrogance begins'.
   Koetef

To have lost a brother is to know a deeper loneliness.
   Bruen

I see no reason to spend good money on newspapers just to read somebody's opinion of what he thinks might have happened, somewhere on a particular occasion.
   Shemak

Life is a bitch – and then you die
   LL

There is plenty of time – all we have to do is wait for it.
   Bruen

If 'Life is Worth Living' – why is it so sodding complicated?
   Koetef

Always see that the main-sheet is clear and cannot get foul of anything in running out. Even the most favoured lady passenger should not be allowed to put her feet on it.
   Earl of Pembroke, 1890

Gunnery instructor's far-carrying bellow

'He's not your friend. You have no friends on the Parade Ground."

Anon

'Me a submariner? Perish the thought!"

Bruen

Life's contract is renewed daily when you wake up (or don't).

Anon

Naval officer, walking out of the Mess with a crate of beer under his arm,

'I do like these packed lunches.'

Bruen

And the sea will grant each man new hope.

Christopher Columbus

A bobstay rings true.

Shemak

Never 'moon' or think about such things as politics, philosophy or people when boat sailing Frivolous conversations on subjects unconnected with the boat or the weather should be sternly discouraged in any but the most familiar waters and in the finest weather.

Earl of Pembroke, 1890

A 'Schoolie' is a type of naval officer who does not know his spurnwater from his dado.

Anon

The more a man possesses, over and above that which he needs, the more careworn he becomes.

GBS

Love is but a song repeated.

Bruen

RN Lieutenant giving a Tidal Efficiency lecture, 13.10.76
'1976 Tide Tables are as rare as rocking-horse teeth.
Anon

Conversation between the Duke d'Escargo and the Dukes Claud and Phillipe DeSisi, the 'Corsican brothers', at King Louis XVI's Ball, 1789.
'What brings you to Paris?'
'Oh, you might say, a little business and a little pleasure.'
'Which do you prefer – business or pleasure?'
'Well, that depends on what you regard as business and what you may regard as pleasure.'
'In Paris we say, "Business is Pleasure".'
'But to us, pleasure is our business.'
'Then your business should be a pleasure, making my pleasure a business.'
'Unless some mistake business for pleasure, while others know no business but pleasure.'
'In that case, Sir, I will show you my business.'
'My pleasure.'

Lt Cdr Y, in charge of the Sonar School: 'This is the Passive Sonar Section.'
BB, 'Right, I'll walk on tip-toe.'
Bruen

Mad scientist at Portland de-gaussing range, talking about keeping the new MCMVs magnetically clean

'So it is up to you to ensure that your sailors bring their hashish on board in plastic bags – not tins.'

    Bruen

Love and reconciliation must be rather like that feeling you get when the Pound sterling is doing well on the International Monetary Market and you've got one in your pocket.

    Anon

The thing I admire most about sport, any sport I ever played, is the cheating. It's very much part of it.

    Barr

Lt Cdr from Captain Weapons Trials: 'Chatham always seems to have the Fire Brigade standing by when we test the AD/AH. I don't know why.'

    Anon

'What is he anyways – *MCD*?'
'No, he's a PTO.'
'What?' A bloody Dockie!
'I shall tell him that.'
'Oh, I know what a PTO is. He is one of those nasty SD characters who puts the fear of God up Midshipmen.'

    GM/BB

It is better to travel hopefully than to arrive!

    Anon

Where there are proper values, there is hope for truth, but where there is truth, it will almost certainly be destroyed and its place given to compromise.

Bruen

Americans! They have voted in Nixon, Reagan and now Bush for President. Why should the rest of the world take them seriously anymore?

Barr

'Why are you sterilising your mines after 28 weeks?'
'Hague Convention and all that.'
'What' 1907?
'But we are British.'
'Did the Russians sign the Hague Convention?'
'No – but we DID.'

Anon

I was in such a big bed last night that I was going up and down doing Lap Track Spacings.

TI

'I reckon that this mine circuit selection is just right for your mentality, Bernie. You are far better at sorting something out of rubbish than the straightforward calculation.'

RM

Seven bells struck as Jack awoke.
His hand was on his midship spoke.

Trad

Seaman C, after being told that the Buffer's decision about his watch change, had been endorsed by the First Lieutenant: 'I'm endorsed!'

Buffer, 'How nice for you.'

Seaman C, 'Hang on, I don't even know what endorsed means.'

Buffer, 'It means you're not allowed out of doors – now get down that hatch!'

Gavinton

'Here, this new deep-freeze. Can't be for us.'

'Why not? It was addressed to us.'

'It must be for another ship.'

'Why do you say that?'

'Well, it's got shelves in it; which means that the Cox'n will not be able to mix the delicate aroma of kippers with the beef.'

Gavinton

'Can you sign R's request for a make-and-mend, please, Sir?'

'He had one last month.'

'Yes, but he has got a good reason for this one. I doubt that you will have heard it before.'

'If I have not-he can have it'.

'Well, he wants a make-and-mend because his dog is dying and he wants to take it to the Vet.'

'I reckon he deserves a week's leave for that one.'

Bruen

The 'in' piece of kit for engineers in 1977 was the Silver Jubilee Clip.

Anon

Things to do in an HMS VERNON office while waiting for 'secure' at the weekend:

Ring your oppo in the next door office while attempting to go through as many exchanges as possible on the military net – Portsmouth, Chatham, Empress State Building, Northwood, MOD Main Building, Empress State again, Rosyth, Faslane, Bath, Devonport, Portland, Portsmouth, Vernon and the number. Thus you would dial: 8131288868513137914121487 2464 or to go the other way about: 81513111811125 86881414872464 which is quicker. Fun, isn't it!

Anon

For pleasures are like poppies spread,
You seize the flower, its bloom is shed.
Or, like the snowflake in a river,
For a moment white then melts for ever.

Burns

There are many words spoken in the cause of truth but very few are relevant. *Midshipman BR, HMS Albion 1970*

'Pass me another Midshipman – this one's split'
'But where will I get another?'
'Open another tin.'

Anon

Engineering officer, HMS ALBION: 'In a Guided Missile Destroyer, engineering problems are technical. Onboard this mighty "hooker" they are agricultural.'

Midshipman GM, 'I wondered why we had a tractor on the flight deck!'

Anon

'The Haig Convention? I like the sound of that. Pour me one while you're at it!'
    Barr

An ancient gunner taught Albion's midshipmen the correct report on closing up the number one multi-barrelled anti-aircraft gun (to be intoned with a distinct rhythm): 'Number one Pompom closed up, cleared away, bores clear, receivers checked.'
    Anon

Surviving as a midshipman is purely a question of mind over matter – they don't mind and you don't matter.
    HMS Albion, 1970

It's not the having that's important – it's the doing.
    Bruen

The colour of this paint you've mixed reminds me of a tart's windowbox.
    Barr

'Line' used as a punishment at Wellington College, 1960s:
    'Nothing is so distressing to a well-regulated mind than to see a boy, who ought to know better, disporting himself at improper moments.'
    Jack Clegg

Captain HMS YARNTON, boarding an oil-drilling rig in Trucial Oman States' waters 1970:
    'You can't drill here, you know.'
    Anon

'Happiness is a well-run chicken farm.'
   Midshipman's Fleet Board, 1970

Shea's Law: On a windless day, when lighting your pipe, the match will blow out.

When we go out – we drink.
When we drink – we get drunk.
When we get drunk – we sleep.
When we sleep – we commit no sin.
When we commit no sin we go to heaven.
So, let's all go out, get drunk and go to heaven.
   PB

When cutting your toenails, don't file them, just throw them away!
   Anon

She was only the Bos'n's Mate's daughter
But her eyes were lovely and bright.
She switches them off each morning
And she switches them on each night.
   Bruen

Make yourself ready in your cabin for the mis-chance of the hour, if so it happens.
   George C. Sears

None is so poor that he need sit on a pumpkin- that is pure shiftlessness.
   Thoreau

Sadly, the most beautiful phrase in the English language is no longer 'I love you' but 'What are you worth?'
   Barr

It takes a heavy hammer to drive a long nail.
   Anon

There ain't no danger in being wrong for a man who has never been right all his life.
   Anon

Merit points make the world go round.
   Anon

Young Cox'n of RAMPART's motor boat upon being challenged by the PO Cox'n of the admirals barge at Cowes:
'That move alongside was suicidal, where are you from?'
Young motorboat Cox'n: 'Birmingham! Why?'
PO Cox'n: 'No, you silly young bugger. What ship?'
   Barr

There are three types of men: those who are alive, those who are dead and those at sea.
   PB

Presentation is 90% of success
   Anon

Midshipman's Board 'questions', HMS ALBION, 1970:
1 'What can you tell me about Marine Auxiliaries?'
   'A fine regiment, Sor!' (said with a tug of the forelock)

2 'What do you do when the power supplies in your 4.5 inch gun turret fall over?'

'Right two chocks, up one wedge and fire on the upward roll!'

3 'Who is responsible for the Electrical Department in your ship?

'The Torpedo Lieutenant, Sir.'

Anon

The practice of testing the fortitude of candidates by removing their underwear is to be discouraged.

BR 177 RN Diving Manual

'Cavet periculo qui etiani tutus cavet.' (He is free from danger who, even when he is safe, is on his guard*)*

Publius Sirius

Mac and BB discussing the various merits of their diving watches

BB, 'Mine's got a scratch-proof face; well, it's crystal.'

Mac, 'I bet yours has not got as good luminosity as mine.'

BB, 'I bet yours hasn't got a spindle that can change the day and the date separately.'

Mac, 'I bet your doesn't ring up your mum when you have had a diving accident!'

Matelots Nursery Rhyme:
Old mother Hubbard went to the cupboard
to get poor Rover a bone.
When she bent over, Rover took over
and slipped her a bone of his own.

Barr

'It's fun, Fun, FUN! It's fun for all the family. Everyone can join in! It's new, it's blue, it's exciting! It's BRIT-EX – it's over!'
HMS Russell, Brit-Ex 71

Notice on Divisional Officer's cabin door, HMS Blake:
'It's all part of the challenge. Keep smiling; it's all free. Every day is Sunday. The sun always shines. It's all downhill and the answer to your next question is, "NO"!'
Bruen

In the public bar of the Lennox:
He: 'Excuse me – but do you collect butterflies' wings?'
She: 'No!'
He: 'Well, that's enough about butterflies' wings; now tell me about yourself.'
She: 'What do you want to know?'
He, calling over his shoulder to his 'oppo': 'What do I say now, Pete?'
Anon

There really are the following birds:
The Scaup – The Smew – The Shikra – The Lammergeier – The Chukar – The American Green-backed Purple Gallinule – The Blue-cheeked Bee Eater – the Bifasculated and Bimaculated Lark – The Red-tailed Black-eared Wheatear – The Sprosser – The Rufous Bushchat – The Fulvous Babbler – The Penduline Tit – The Orange-tufted Nile Valley Pygmy Sun-bird – The Red-eyed Viriole – The Slate coloured Junko – The Syrian Serin – The Dead Sea Scrub Sparrow – The Laughing Gull – and Tristram's Grackle.
Bruen

When forethought is a characteristic of the sailor, his lot will rapidly amend. That, however, is almost too much to hope for.
Frank T. Bullen FRGS, 1899

It seems that the Royal Navy's no longer full of 'men' but instead, is made up of 'personnel'.
Bruen

If work is so damned good for you, why do we need 'injury lawyers'?
Barr

Lookout reporting a sighting to the Bridge:
'Bridge!'
'Lights dead ahead – far, Sir.'
OOW: 'Roger. You are looking at the Island of Malta.'
Lookout: 'Good! When can we open fire?'
Anon

'Is that ship called "San-da-lion" or "San-dallion"?'
   "San-dillion". It's British; they can change the pronunciation.'
   'In that case it is probably called "Sarsnia"!'
   Anon

PARKING VIOLATION
   This is not a parking ticket but, if it were in my power, you would receive two. Because of your bullheaded, inconsiderate, feeble attempt at parking, you have taken enough room for a twenty mule team, two elephants, a goat and a safari of pygmies. The reason for giving you this is so that, in the future, you may think of someone else other than yourself. Besides, I don't like domineering, egotistical or simple-minded drivers and you

probably fit into one, if not all, of these categories. I sign off wishing you an early transmission-failure on the motorway at about 4.30am.

Colonel Spittle

'You can't take that yacht to sea, you have not got an RYA certificate!'
'I have a better qualification than that.'
'Oh yes, what?'
'I own it!'

Anon

'I knew that I should not have had that sixth bottle of Raki!'

Lieutenant Richard Headon, RN

Outward Bound Course Instructor pointing out very steep hill, covered in pine trees:
'You'll enjoy this, lads, a nice, gentle hill to start with.'
'If it is that gentle, why is it camouflaged?'

Bruen

Same instructor, after pointing out various types of gull to his course: 'Quick, lads, what kind of gull is that?'

Chorus: 'A SEA-gull!'

Bruen

Matelots Nursery Rhyme:
Humpty Dumpty sat on a wall.
Humpty Dumpty had a great fall.
He broke both arms, he broke both legs,
And during the fall he shit his 'kegs'

Barr

A Diving Officer, walking down main passageway, dressed in wet-suit trousers, training shoes, khaki shirt, belt and diver's 'short-sword' knife, is stopped by a Royal Marine:
'What are you doing today, Sir ... Hamlet?'

Bruen

HMS BULWARK visits the West Indies; the following axiom abounds:
'Can't crack me. I'm ARUBA duck!'

Anon

Conversation between Captain and the Geordie Gunner's Yeoman,
'I have been looking at your target for the shoot today.'
'Way-aye, Sir.'
'Will it capsize, do you think?'
'It'll get blown to shite, like.'

Anon

Kirkliston to Gavinton in the calm of the morning, after a very rough night: 'Matthew Ch 8, vs 26'.
[And he said unto them, 'Why are you afraid, oh men of little faith?' Then he arose and rebuked the winds and the sea and there was a great calm.]

Gavinton to Kirkliston: 'Matthew Ch 8, vs 27'.
[And the men marvelled, saying, 'What manner of man is this that even the winds and the sea obey him?']

Bruen

Ship's weekly quiz question: 'What are the Seven Wonders of the World?' elicited, among others, the following answers:

'The 'Boom!' disco in Corfu', 'the northern lights of old Aberdeen' and 'the concrete cows of Milton Keynes'.
HMS GAVINTON, 1984

Matelots Nursery Rhyme (Dittie)
I'm looking over my dead dog Rover
As he's laying on the kitchen floor.
One leg's broken, another one's lame,
He's been run over by a railway train.
It's no use denying the poor dogs dying,
As he's laying on the kitchen floor.
Now I'm looking out for old mother Hubbard,
Coz I know that she'll be feelin' sore!
Anon

Piraeus rat-catching dog, Jim, would not eat bacon or sausages, but loved grapes. *Anon*

Visitor to Senior Officer, in hospital with a 'nasty'
'Good morning, Sir. How are you feeling?'
'Croak!'
'I just popped in to give you this paper weight. I'll put it on top of your letter so it does not blow away.'
'Croak!'
'Anything I can get you? Any messages?'
'Croak!'
'Everything's fine with the ships.'
'Croak.' (Wink).
'Well, goodbye, Sir.'
'Croak.'
Anon

1984, Gulf of Suez Mine Clearance. Gavinton's steering fails and she uses steering sails to return to Base.

'All seaman hands lay aft. Stand-by to reduce sail.'

'Get the Spanker off her, if you please, Mr Bos'n.'

'Aye-aye, Cap'n!'

> Bruen

Midshipman to navigator on bridge: 'Do you want to come downstairs for some supper?'

Navigator: 'What!?*!?*!'

> Anon

Signal from Gavinton to remainder of Gulf of Suez Clearance Squadron at the end of the operation: 'Deuteronomy Chapter 26, vs 6-8.' *[And the Egyptians laid upon us hard bondage and the Lord brought us out of Egypt.]*

> Bruen

Captain's 'dit' for calling the hands on leaving for homeward bound: 'Fair stands the wind for Albion. Gibraltar lies before us. We've travelled far beneath yon Star, – Far from the Eye of Horus.

First Lieutenant changes last line to read, 'Leaning on the Pelorus.'

> Anon

Headline in newspaper after ships return from Gulf of Suez Clearance:

'FIDDLER OF THE FLEET FIGHTS CURSE OF THE RED SEA' Falklands Hero – Another Daring Escapade.

> Bruen

Captains 'dit' for calling the hands on another occasion:
'Good morning all you sleepy folk. Mount Etna is in sight, with smoke and flame and pumice stone a-spouting in the night. If Etna is in sight, my boys, then surely it must be, that fair Augusta's close at hand, where we can get some fuel – and water – but no mail – sorry!'
   Anon

Leading Cook Husted's Athol Brose:
   Soak 8oz of porridge oats in water overnight. Strain and press liquid out. Make half the oats into porridge and eat. Retain the other half of the oats and blend them with the liquid, six teaspoons of honey, four tots of whisky and a pint of cream.
   Bruen

Ex PO Tug Wilson, in Dartmoor pub, as more and more of his friends poured in to celebrate his birthday:
   'Sure is a high tide today.'
   TW

Captain (on bridge) to Rubber Boat recovering a spent torpedo:
'Cox'n, mind the propellers on that torpedo, they may be sharp.'
Rubber Boat: 'Pffftttsssssss!'
   Bruen

Message on Cook's menu card, HMS GAVINTON:
   'Pick-n-mix. You pick the tin and we'll open it, even fish. Take it easy, eat it and don't ever mention fish or tins again.'

Captain to newly-joined Leading Hand: 'Your job is to pick the boys up for haircuts; mine is to drive the ship fast alongside the wall.'

Leading Hand: 'Well, you're going to have an easy day then, Sir.'

    Anon

Plymouth Clearance Diving Team training session:

Police arrive at HMS DRAKE pier having 'had a report of a man escaping cross the mud'!

    Anon

BB, entering Thistle Park tavern Devonport, sings to landlord Harry Hartop (to the tune 'Oh what a beautiful morning):

'Oh what a beautiful afternoon,

out in the sun I will soak.

I've got a wonderful feeling

that I'll have a pint of Royal Oak

and a 'packet of pig' and a 'chilli'

and no doubt some comments quite silly.

Oh, I am quite happy. What about you?

And, instead of just one pint, I'll probably have two.'

Harry: 'Oh dear! The Oak's just gone cloudy!'

    Bruen

North Sea yacht race. Gavinton is safety and committee boat.

Civilian starter: 'I say, Captain, my starting guns seem to be blackening your paintwork.'

Captain: 'That's all right. I'll get a man up.'

Civilian starter: 'That's awfully decent of you.'

Captain: 'To fill you in!'

BB unexpectedly walks into Swan Hotel Devonport:
Fiddler Jennings; 'Get out! Go back to Scotland!'
BB; 'But why?'
FJ; 'Because I have just written you a nine page letter, that's why.'
  Bruen

The following are from HMS GAVINTON's shakes book:
(1) Yesterday I put my 22 years' notice in.
(2) Be a mug – join a tug.
(3) There once was an ugly duckling – 'til some bastard shot it.
(4) Dear God, can you wake me up now?
(5) Once upon a time, there were three bears. Now there is only one – due to the fur trade.
(6) Dead men tell no tales. In fact, they don't say anything at all.
(7) Trooping the Colour is not a form of racial hatred in the RN.
(8) Hear about the matelot who thought that Greenpeace was a form of VD? (Not bad for 2 o'clock in the morning.)
(9) If I die in battle, please don't bury me at sea; I can't swim. Nor cremate me; dust makes me sneeze.
(10) 0645. Shake 1st Lt. You Know Where! Hot cup of tea with one sugar would be very nice. It would wake me up in a charming mood which would last all day. Thank you.

Message passed clearly and slowly on Channel 16 to US Navy Bulk Tanker Sealift Arctic after she had passed two cables ahead of warship patrolling the Straits of Hormuz:
   'Sealift Arctic, this is Omani warship on patrol. The International Regulations for the Prevention of Collision at Sea clearly state that an overtaking vessel should keep well clear of the vessel being overtaken until past and clear. Your action in

passing that close across my bows is in violation of the Regulations and is considered unseamanlike and rude. Out.'

Upon winning a High Court Judgement in The Strand 1978 and being ordered to pay £900 costs:
'That's British Justice for you. Imagine what it might have cost us had we lost?'
   Barr

On the beat-up to Prince Charles' wedding, a TV interviewer investigated the wedding cake being made at HMS Pembroke.

Interviewer to junior cook trainee: 'What's navy cake like? Do you enjoy it?'
Trainee: 'Oh yes, it's very good.'

'1981 makes 1984 look like 1968'
   BB

Swedish ship Anna approaches South Shields hailing station:
'What ship?'
'Anna'
'What ship?'
'Anna.'
'What ship? What ship?'
'Anna.Anna!'
'Ah kna' ya kna' but Ah wanna kna' an' ah dan't kna'!'
   Anon

From my air-conditioned bayte,
In my air-conditioned car,
To my air-conditioned office in Wudam,

I'm an air-conditioned Mercenary,
A real old Dog of War;
Ilhamdulillah, wagit zayne,
I'm fighting for Oman.
  (*written by a 'real' Oman mercenary*)

Matelots Nursery Rhyme:
Mary Mary quite contrary,
How does your garden grow?
With silver bells and cockle shells
And the answer to your next question is, 'No!'
  Barr

Pass-words:
'The purple aardvarks are flying south for the winter.'
'Yes but the little yellow golliwog has lost his trouser button.'
'Surely the grip of the Prendergasp will soon weaken.'
'Only if Mount Paltipid is made of brattle-tids.'

Two songs from young Omani sailors:
1. 'Welcome SEEB (ship). Thank you for the good exercises.'
2. 'The Captain came on board, gave an order, said, "We go to sea." The sea was rough but we said, "Yes, Siddi, we go!"

Signal from Commodore, at end of exercise, to OTC:
  'Interrogative final gun?'
  Signal from OTC: 'BANG!'

A Pint of Hicks reaches the parts that Heineken never can.
  Barr

The Rule of Three:
Birds: Sparrows, eagles and shite-hawks.
Fish: Goldfish, Herrings and Mackerel.
Flowers: Daisies, lilies and roses.
Animals: Tigers, dogs and mice.
Them that walks, them that runs and them that slinks.
Reptiles: Snakes, crocodiles and dragons.
Them that walks, them that swims and them that slithers.
People: Them as is hopeless, them as is helpless and them as is useless.
Instruments: Those you blow, those you bang and those you scrape.
Land: Mountains, plains and valleys: What you walk up, across or down.

> *Bruen/Barr*

A yacht is a hole in the water, lined with wood, into which you throw all your money.

> *Anon*

If you have something that is soft when fresh, it will go hard. If it is crisp when fresh, it will go soggy.

> *Anon*

HMS SOLEBAY, Atlantic Ocean, 1958
Officer of the Watch: 'Helmsman! What course are you supposed to be steering?
Helmsman: 310` Sir!
Officer of the Watch: Then why is the ships head pointing 330`?
Helmsman: I'll get on to it right away. Sir!
Officer of the Watch: (Reply unsuitable for public consumption)

A: 'The best place to get films developed is the Apollo Studio in Ruwi High Street.'
B: 'The Apollo Studio? Is that next to the Adonis Health and Massage Parlour?'
C: 'A-donis? Would you mind? I am THE-donis!'

A reason: The explanation of the motivation of the perpetration of an act.

An excuse: The justification of the explanation of the motivation of A the perpetration of an act.

A lame excuse: The imagination of validity in the justification of the explanation of the motivation of the perpetration of an act.

Matelots Nursery Rhyme:
Little Jack Horner stood in a corner,
Spanking his little old monkey.
Soon he was seen, if you know what I mean,
To be rigged like a Portuguese donkey.
   Barr

C.O.: 'Here we are, a few days before inspection and, quite frankly, I have nothing to do.'
Bos'n: 'Yes, it's always like that. The best thing to do is to get a Land Rover and a couple of cans of beer and piss off inland and throw bricks at the sand.'

Having returned from sailing a modern competition yacht:
   'They're just racing space-blobs; great for round the buoys but they could never heave-to.'
   CW

JJS: discussing music, to passer-by:
'Bill, how does the Irish Guards march-past go?'
'Left-roit, left-roit, left-roit.'

With four water-spouts in the immediate vicinity, C.O. to X.O.:
'I wonder what it's like to be in the middle of a water-spout.'
'Wet!'

One half of a telephone conversation heard in Oman:
'You do not know me but, if you look at me again, your body
will be under my car and you will not return to England; only
your body!'

Life without music is beautiful without the 'U' – Hard Stone
Feathers.
    Koetef

Starboard ten! Morning men. Where's the bleedin' Buffer then?
    Heslop

Sharks? You don't swim in their water and they don't drink in
your pub.
    M.R-M.

Amelcards and Ocletrapes lure KO!
    Koetef

Have you ever tried to buy shoelaces in a land where nobody
wears shoes?
    JC

From a Captain's night order book:
'Blow me if it comes on to shake!'
  DW

A Naval cocktail party: 'A room full of Flumellies and Petty Boblecokes whose nauseous meetings abound with loathsome flies and gaseous platitudes.'
  Bruen

Play it as though you mean it!
  Fiddler Jennings

Tiz good 'ere, innit!
  Bill Seymour

Life in the Oman Navy is like an harmonica – all suck and blow. HQ do all the blowing – we are the suckers.
  JJS

Notice on the shoreside telephone:
  'Please do not call the operator when he is busy with the message. Wait until he attends you.'

'The ship is rolling too much. Secure everything"
  SA

Beer, women and song are all of no use to you if they are flat.
  Barr

It's easier to crack a cryptic crossword than to understand a Cornishman giving a foreigner road directions.
  Barr

If 'Stores' were meant to give out equipment, they would be called 'Issues'.

Anon

The Duke of Wellington, remarking on the terrible state of the country left by his soldiers, and being informed that the damage was actually caused by local children:

'That there be such men – first there must be these.'

BB (from a dream)

'HQ certainly has its finger on the pulse'

'Yes, but you do not usually take the pulse with both thumbs on the carotid artery.'

'Sailors come in types – recognisably A, B, C, D and E. – and then there's type "F"!' 'And THEY are all in my division.

CW and GB

'Here's to the land. May it always fall where it ought!

Bruen

Voice from above Montague Whaler beached on a shingle bank:

'There's rocks over there!'

'There's rocks all over the world.'

'But you are on a falling tide.'

'Don't we know it!'

'Tough as Teak' TM

Matelots Nursery Rhyme:

Little Bo Peep has lost her sheep
And doesn't know where to find them!

Then tell her to go to the galley below
They should just about finished a'fryin' em.
    Barr

'Honour those the dragons heed in thought and favour, word
and deed. Worlds are lost or worlds are saved from those
dangers dragon-braved.'
    Dragon Flight

Windup Telephone Call No.1
'Is that Chief Petty Officer Barr?'
'Yes.'
'THE Chief Petty Officer Barr?'
'It is.'
'The one who runs all the expeditions and mountaineering?'
'Yes'
'Well, I don't want to talk about that now.'
'Oh How can I help you then?'
'Have you got any canoe instructors? I mean, who would you say
was your best canoeing instructor?'
Pause.
'Hello Bernie, What do you want?'

Windup Telephone: 2
'Hello, Chief Barr speaking.'
'Could I speak to the boxing coach, please?'
'Sorry, you have the wrong number.'
'But, isn't he there?'
'No, you have to ring 24151.'
'Well, is there anyone there I could speak to?'
Pause.

'Hello Bernie, you sod – that's the second time you've got me today!'

Do Thames Wherry-men have sprit personalities?
   Shemak

Women are like the sea – capricious. You haven't a clue what they are going to do next.
   Bruen

When religion enters – reason departs.
   Koetef

What I say is distorted by what you hear.
What you hear is distorted by what I say.
Everything else is just noise.
   Barr

You are better off being ashore, wishing you were aboard, than being aboard wishing you were ashore.
   SH

'The whole place lends itself. It's sort of made for the way he's done it.'
   AC, on GP's workshop

'Roll like a bastard and slam like a "V"!'
   (*Popular saying in MCMVs.*)

When you're a fighter – you're different.
   PK, ABA and Navy Light Welterweight Champion.

'Legiron's' Holywell Mustard:

4 oz mustard powder. 4 teaspoons chilli-wine. 2 capfuls Glen Morangie. 20 shakes Tabasco. 14 shakes Worcestershire sauce. 8 shakes Garlic Salt. 8 heaped teaspoons horseradish sauce.

This is an excellent hot mustard that does wonders to the taste of food.

If you're talking of your rum, you're drinking two-and-one. Chiefs and POs will drink it 'neaters'; But your stomach must be tough when the sea's getting rough and you have a greasy dinner from the heaters. For it's rum, rum, rum; fill my belly full of rum. You can keep your French vermouth; just fill my hollow tooth. With that wonderful elixir called rum.
   Tug Wilson

Nothing quite matches the suppressed excitement exhibited by young men who are about to go to sea for the very first time, loading victuals and stores into their ship.
   Bruen

Life is a bitch – and then you marry one.
   SB

The only reason a woman has legs is to get her from the bedroom to the kitchen and back.
   HE

I will not buy my kids books – in case they don't read them.
   RM Bandsman

'My watch keeps perfect time. It doesn't lose even a second in a week.'

'So, how come you were late for both watches this morning?'

Having a child is the ultimate conceit.
Bruen

She: 'What was that story you told the other night?'
He: 'Oh, that's a terrible joke.'
She: 'Well, tell it anyway.'
And he did. And it was.
Anon

Heard in a Restaurant, where kids were noisily misbehaving:
"Those children should be put in the deep-freeze for half an hour"
"If they were mine, they would be dead all over the pavement."

The majority of people are scarcely entertaining. A very few are genuinely witty. But most tiresome are those who believe they are amusing – but are not.
JAB

To receive a blow-job is to demonstrate the extremity of trust.
Shemak

BB, on a Sigma 38 yacht
"There are two good things about them: they go well to windward and they have nice grab-handles."
And: "If they're so good – why are there so many for sale?"

The young must always be stout-hearted.
The 'Otters'

Matelots Nursery Rhyme
Hickory Dickory Dock
The mouse ran up the clock.
He said, 'here now look you',
as he shagged the Welsh cuckoo.
Hickory Dickory Dock.
Barr

How nice it must be to fall into the arms of a woman but how unfortunate to fall into her hands.
MP

It must be awful to be an Argentinian and to know that your country's sole contribution to world culture is the Tango.
NAB.

Peter Tavy Inn, Dartmoor, Christmas 1977 during a hard winter: BBC Evening News.
"A snow-plough has been lost on Exmoor, but they are sending a helicopter to find it.'
Later. "They've lost the helicopter!"

Man entering from the snow-storm outside;
By! but it ain't 'arf 'festive' out there."

A woman, accompanied by a small boy, was discovered sniffing suspiciously at a five-star Hotel's buffet;
Waiter; "Is it bad?"
Woman; "I'm sorry?"

"The food – is it bad?"

"Oh, no, but I 'm seeing if my son would like it. He's very sensitive about what he eats."

"If I was you, I'd just fill a plate and tell him to finish it."

"I suppose you always finish your food."

"Correct."

Woman to son: "Now, this is cheesy potato. You'll like that."

"Of course he will, That's what I'm having."

Boy responds with: "I'm glad you're not MY dad."

Tall ship at sea – wind on the nose.
    WP

The Times is not normally found in the hands of the illiterate.
    SherlockHolmes

A Naval Rating walks into Devonport Dockyard, bursting for a pee, and asks a dockyard matey

"Where's the urinal?"

"I don't know. How many funnels has it got?"

Matelots Nursery Rhyme
The grand old Duke of York,
He had ten thousand men
He marched them up to the top of the hill
And he marched them down again.
And when they were up they were up
And when they were down they were down,
And when they were only half way up,
Naturally, they were in the middle.
    Barr

When I clap my hands behind a fly, it knows, the instant before its death, that all hope is lost.

Bruen.

The day I start to grow up is the day I start to die.

'Boy'

If music makes the world go round – then we are trading on the past.

Bruen

There is nothing more depressing than a miserable Trainee.

Shemak

Circumcision – a peculiar type of mutilation visited by parents upon their sons – from which neither derives any benefit. The parents, as observers, may feel some momentary pangs of righteousness but the son, in that stab of pain, is sentenced to a lifetime's speculation.

'Boy'

Time is like a cheap boarding-house clock – counting seconds with the motes of dust floating in the air. Yet to some it is a trumpet blast that shouts, "Take all you can but fight me for every moment!"

Koetef

"On the great issues of today where does the Labour Party stand? Aside."

David Frost, TW3

Being required to talk while having nothing to say is to appear a fool.
  Bruen

"Beckie! Watch Channel 3. This bloke's just tore off this other bloke's arm. It's brilliant! Now he's melted!"
  MC

Climax – a phenomenon experienced weekly by TV actors.
  Barr.

Adolescence – a taste of despair among the bitter fruits of youth. For even adolescence holds no promise of fulfilment when confronted by its suppressed desire and hopeless longings.
  Koetef.

Police Officer to sailor whilst investigating the disappearance of Deck Chronometers from a ship:
"Now, what can you tell me about these watches?"
"Bloody magic. One-in-six!"
  HMS Gavinton

Flutterin' and dancin' in the breeze, Daffodils – Stand at Ease!
  BP.

"Here's a song for Welshmen everywhere – preferably in Wales!"
  GH

Breakfast time, after a particularly good party
"You were well away last night."

"Yes, but at least I'm not still saying, 'Fizz woosh glug-glug ching-ching'!"
Bruen

Effective warning notice.
'BEEWHAIRE! WHETT WYTE PAYNTE BEALOE'

"How do you tell the difference between an adult badger and a juvenile one?"
"An adult badger will probably be working in the House of Lords."
RA

Competence – demonstrating the ability to deceive.
Incompetence – the ability to display a total lack of stress during an emergency.
Barr

Expressions used in RN Mine-hunter of the 1970s:
'*Cow-bag:*' A piece of mine-sweeping equipment that refuses to behave itself on recovery.
'*Crow*' A sailor temporarily lacking in value.
'*Great crow*' A sailor temporarily worthless.
'*Preece! Come here, you little rat!*' A method of summoning the sweep-storesman from below.
Clap your hands on that.' A signal for men to applaud before recovering a tow by hand.
'*In the Buffery/axery/scrubbery etc.*' Answer to 'Where's the Buffer/axe/scrubber etc?'
'*Leave. Leave your selves alone!*'. Normal start of shore-leave pipe (announcement).

'First Lieutenant to the Bridge – at your convenience.'. Broadcast made by the Captain indicating trouble with visiting Staff-officers and requirement for diversionary tactics
Bruen

Here we are in 1993 and you still can't beat an E-type Jaguar for sheer style.
WJR

Junior Seaman "Where are all the Squeejees? -
Leading Hand, In the Squeejeree, marked 'S' – where do you think?
Barr

Perhaps the chicken is the egg's way of reproducing itself!
Anon

If you pull the wings off a Fly, what do you get? A Walk.
BC

New Year's eve was the depressing festival of concealed regret it is anywhere on earth.
Roland Huntsford, 'Shackleton'

One British Officer to another, about an Omani Officer,
"...but you're senior to him."
"That counts for little. I don't have a moustache."

SB describes the rigging and high-tech gizmos found in modem racing yachts:
'Technical devices for eroding seamanship skills.'

Commercial airlines – a not very magic carpet ride.
SJ.

Heard during Ramadan:
   'What are you doing on board Steward? You are not on duty."
   "No, Sir. I've brought the extra rations for the Fasting."

'*Doing a Moon-rise*' is an American expression for watching the planet ascend above the horizon. Misinterpreted as 'exhibiting one's naked posterior while maintaining an erection.'

"Jimmy's going ballistic"
   An RN expression meaning that the First Lieutenant is not appreciative of the situation and requires immediate rectification action.

He was obliged, however, to throw over Christianity. Those who base their conduct upon what they are, rather than upon what they ought to be, always must throw it over in the end.
   EM Forster

JN, (American) on the workings of a Middle-eastern Navy,
   "Of course it is all done with smoke and mirrors, ya know."

Of all the Watches, in their way,
The one I like the best,
I'll take the Forenoon any day,
And bugger all the rest!
   Bruen

The Statue of Liberty stands with one hand aloft, holding a foaming Coke can and the other in her pocket fingering England's money; her back is firmly turned to America.

John Riding, 'Sea Egg'

Matelots Nursery Rhyme:
Little Miss Muffet sat on her tuffet,
Eating her curds and whey.
When down came a glider,
And landed beside her,
And it's pilot had her away.

Barr

Belief in God and a Life at Sea are incompatible. To assume that supplication to an insubstantial being will deliver one from adversity is self-deluding and counter-productive to the ethos of survival.

Bruen

The prayers of the Mattawah, no matter how raucous, fervent or compelling, cannot compete with the swooping play of the passing dolphin.

Koetef

"All those cheap Italian hinges are breaking. Please order some more."
"Yes. This time we'll get cheap French ones."

What women do on similar occasions defies belief – but, as they are women, this is of little consequence.

Shemak

MF, when asked by a Senior Officer about his conversation with a particularly pedantic Ambassador

"Fortunately for me, Sir, the Ambassador has many interesting things to say."

MF

Q. What signal must a vessel exhibit by day to indicate that she is engaged in sailing?
A. One or more large pieces of canvas, hoisted into the rigging where they can best be seen.
[A question that isn't, but should be, in the Rule of the Road exam]

Bruen

Song sung by Omani sailors, invited to take a Zodiac rubber boat to the shore across a spit of land and to rejoin the ship on the other side: (while portaging the craft)
"The camel has carried us – now we must carry the camel."

RB, in a letter, "….we have a Form-teacher from Hell!"

World War One naval officers' saying, when life became tense:
"Who wouldn't sell his little farm and go to sea?"

Bartimeus

Suez Canal Pilot, on boarding a Barquentine in the Great Bitter Lakes
"Very bad view on this ship. Bad for navigation."
"This is the Chart-room."
Steps up half a deck
"There is not enough visibility here. This is dangerous."
"Yes, this is the Wheel-house."

Steps up another half a deck into the open air.
"Where is the Bridge?"
"This IS the Bridge."
    Bruen

Rule of Single Probability Interface
When wearing an analogue watch, one will only ever check the date at a quarter past the hour or fifteen seconds after the minute.
    Bruen

Very small girl, to guest she has surprised about to get dressed, (pointing to mid-section): "What's that?"
    Guest, a little taken-aback but striving to appear in command of the situation: It's a todger."
    "No it's not. Todgers are MUCH bigger than that."

CB: "I can remember our teacher pointing out the date to us one day – quite special – 4-5-65."
BB, "Well, that's nice; but 4-5-67 would have been more special."
    CB "It WAS 4-5-67!"

Then there's Bernie Bruen who not only rides bikes, but thinks he is one, as those of you who went to Sur last year will remember.
    'Sabco' Sue.

Kuwait airport, 15 12 94: The Transit lounge is decorated with small potted trees. One – a marijuana plant – is placed in the NO SMOKING area.

There are many people who deny the fact that there is life after death; however their denial has no ground, rather a mere speculation, which is based on pure conjecture.
An anonymous churchman

The only time a woman should get out of bed is when she goes to get more coal. *JH*

DP. "I bought a Japanese iron. The instructions were in Norwegian."
RH. "Must be a travelling-iron."

The Racing Rules – unseamanlike behaviour in yachts.
Bruen

It is fashionable to own and use a quantity of golf clubs; however, the apogee of skill lies in requiring just three.
Shemak

Layman's Terms
Referring to the above reference, we would like to notify you that after new certificates issued which have been equalled with the Ministry of Education Certificates according to the Ministry's decree No.(40/91) we have started to forward educational course results of the Ministry of Education according to what have been agreed to be as documents for (armed forces) personnel when they require to equal their certificates or to continue studying. (Air-force) personnel faced difficulties to

forward the results to the Ministry of Education due to units and Regiments did not obligate to what has been mentioned in Reference A above and to fill Annex A, which is enclosed with our letter and mentioned to every candidate for joining levels three and four of Arabic language. It is regretted to refer that results and certificates of personnel attending courses will not be issued as soon as possible unless schools, centres and units be provided with information required which stated at Part B of Annex A is respect of English Language knowing that the course duration is four months and this information is supposed to be available for the students when they join the educational courses. It is necessary to whom are concerned, to fill Part B of Annex A for the personnel who have courses in English language and to forward it to schools at centres or units when their personnel join the courses. This will enable the certificates to be issued as soon as possible and to send the results to Ministry of Education. It is requested to complete Annex A for all courses and send it to authorised concerned to unable us to get the results and certificates.

Enclosed herewith a copy of Reference A above for action. (from Staff Officer Training and Education, Royal Navy of Oman, [promoted to Commander])

"The trouble with this Province today is there's two thirds the people – don't know what the other half's doing."
   Rev Ian Paisley NI

"Anyone who's not confused doesn't know what's going on."
   Rev. I Paisley NI

Navigating Officer, "What's that coffee-cup doing on the chart table?

Officer of the Watch (in a whisper), "The Admiral left it there."

Navigating Officer (sotto voice) "Get these charts off the Admiral's coffee-table!"

They had a baby now – to fuss over, mould in their own image, instil with guilt from the earliest possible moment.

James Lovegrove – 'The Hope'

Banks will lend you as many umbrellas as you like – when the sun is shining; but as soon as it starts to rain they want them all back.

MR-M

Put your trust in log-line and compass and thank the Lord for non-stick pans.

Shemak

It is the presence of the artist that makes the difference between being nude and being naked.

Anon

Each man is at the centre of his universe. It is futile to imagine that he cares for aught within another's sphere for he cannot while remaining faithful to himself. To demonstrate credible concern is merely to conceal a deeper yearning for personal reward.

Boy

When I sound the horn of my new 4x4 – it goes 'Jeep – Jeep'.
Bruen

New Zealand is England as it should be – but hasn't got the time.
Heremana

We are not so poor that we have to make our own music.
A Kiwi

Marmite for girls – Bovril for boys.
Shemak.

"Abdullah, let me buy you a drink."
"No thank you, I want to enjoy myself."

"There's a red light (ahead), Sir!"
"I haven't stopped at a red light since Port Said in 1920."
JR-J as Sir Lancelot Spratt.

My luck is a flower, scattered into a thorn-bush
And gathered barefoot on a very windy day.
Khalid

The flowers of the Sea may be gathered in the Wind,
For there are no Thorns hidden in the passing Waves.
Koetef

Workshop Manager discussing 'shocking pink' spray-job on Omani Mercedes: 'It's so bright I have to get these special sunglasses for the paint sprayers."
"How does it look?"

"I don't know – feels alright though – a bit wet!"
HE

BB. "Have you seen X's house? I couldn't dust all those ornaments every day."
BK. "You don't live in a house. You live in a shed!"

EJ – "Bloody civilians – not organised."
TB. "But you have to marry one!"

Change is the illusion of progress.
  Bruen

She couldn't sail but made a fair cup of tea.
  JH

What is the most disgusting word in the world? – BODY
  LRB

A signal, corrected by first one other, and then re-corrected by a second, finally read – 'Minimise traffic on this circuit.'
  Royal Jubilee Fleet Revue, Sultanate of Oman, 1995

I don't think you quite believe that women exist. To you they are a kind of difficult boy with surplus flesh in some places and missing flesh in others. I'm not sure you even enjoy their company but then I don't know if you ever enjoyed anyone else's either – including your own.
  J to A, 'The Liar' – Stephen Fry

Great Aunt Constance started learning Italian at the age of 97. When asked why, she replied that she 'thought it might prove useful in later life' – and she got five years use of it.

Bruen

Born in February 1875 two years before Great Aunt Constance (1877–1978) Jeanne Calment (121) is the oldest person ever. When asked by a twat-ish news reporter what she thought her future might be, Mme Calment replied, "Short!"

Bruen

XO to Navigator: "Where's your knife?"
Navigator, "I don't carry a knife. I have a pager."

BB "I don't mind sexual deviation; it's the sexual deprivation that gets me."
CB "Except that we don't get enough of it."

The Royal Navy is a praying mantis – it eats its young.

Heremana

The Englishman's home used to be his castle; then it became his fortress, now it's a millstone round his neck.

Koetef

In my opinion, it's a wise father that sends his son to sea... I think!

Barr

The RN's method of officer management consists of getting you over a barrel and either buggering you or just not bothering.

Bruen

Letter from junior RNO officer to senior RNO officer:
　Sir,
1.　I had the honour to do that on behalf of you and in fact that was nothing at all.
2.　I am looking forward always for anything you might think of, so that I will be the first man to do it.
3.　My flag always showing smile for life, life will smile for you and the day light must come once to take behind its dark.
4.　My special regards to (your ship) and her sailors.

Is this Zanussi? Right grid reference – wrong planet.
　'Royal'

Live abroad? Good heavens no. Abroad is beastly. Beastly food. Garlic. Stuffy rooms and guttural squawks. Men kissing each other on the cheek and waving their arms.
　H Rowland

American couple in car touring Scotland; man speaks:
"Excuse me, we're lost. Can you tell us the way to Portree?"
Fiddler, "Aye, ye tak th' firrst left, thun richt, thun left agin. Folla tha' road an' ye'll be thair."
Woman, "We're from Idaho."
Fiddler, "Aye, thun ye really are lost."

"When you're having a really dreadful day, Bernie walks in like a ray of sunshine."
　Jethro

How will today's students recognise the smell of sulphur dioxide when they have never come across a rotten egg? (Health and Safety you know)

Bruen

Vegetarianism is a disease of affluent young white women and certain obscure Asian religious sects. It bears no relationship to reality.

CW

Bernie? He's a minefield of information.

Barr

Them's as dies'll be the lucky ones.

Long John Silver

To be referred to as 'Boss' by Clearance Divers used to be the ultimate accolade. Sadly, it has become the universal substitute for the ubiquitous "Sir".

Bruen

Every human being should be a Muslim.
Islam is the only religion respected by God.
Human beings are not created for any other purpose

His Eminence. Sheikh Ahmed bin Hamed al Khalili, Grand Mufti of Oman.

Your Jeep's dirty, Bern."
"I never clean it – just spray it with oil every so often."
"You should get a Land Rover. They spray themselves automatically."

JM

Heard at Jethro's Carvery – 3.4.96
"There's going to be an eclipse of the moon tonight."
"Oh? What's that all about, then?"
"It's when the sun passes between the moon and the earth."
"Be a bit hot, won't it?"
"No. It's alright. It happens at night."
   Bruen

Cooking requires no intelligence. If it did, women would be no good at it.
   JR

"On entering the gate, one of the dogs which had followed us from the factory, being nearly as hungry as ourselves killed a chicken which occasioned not a little stir and led us to be caged up for the best part of the day in the middle of the only square, and pelted diligently by the inhabitants with rotten eggs and bad oranges – soft things, no doubt, but not the less trying to the temper."
   Arthur Macmurrough Kavanagh, Astrabad, Persia, 11.10.1849

Matelots Nursery Rhyme;
Stoker Simon met a pie man going to the fair.
Said Stoker Simon to the pie man, 'Can I taste your ware?'
The pie man said to Stoker Simon 'only if you've a penny'.
Said Stoker Simon to the pie man 'alas sir, I have not any, It's a non-pay week you see, but if you don't hand over a pastie this minute you miserable little shit, I won't tell your tale to my kids anymore.
   Barr

"What does DHL stand for?"
"I don't know. What does DHL stand for?"
"The Association of Dyslexic People."
   Jethro

If fish have a memory span of only a few seconds, do flying-fish actually enjoy the sensation of flight? Whee... This is fun. Oh crikey, I'm going to crash. Mmm, this is nice I've not been here before...
   Koetef

Said of a disliked senior officer:
   "I'm really looking forward to not seeing him again."
   Bruen

Masseuse 'You can do this yourself you know You can practice self-massage.'
Man 'I already do – on occasions.'

A critic is a person who lacks the talent of the person he is condemning.
   Barr

Found in a Spanish hyper-market
   Contraceptives selling under the brand name 'Family-PLUS'!

and there are Fluttermouses (bats)
   GS

"You're just a girl. What do you know about make-up?"
   Bowie

She, explaining a certain verbosity.
 "Unfortunately I'm a hairdresser."
He, taking his hand off his hip.
 "Fortunately I am not."

Sailor to Master at Arms, when asked why he is appearing at Defaulters' Table: "Ah must'a missed a muster, Master, must'nt'ah?"

I knew that my father finally realised I was handicapped when he sent me off to join the Navy.
 Barr

Many of the Ten Commandments are still relevant today.
 (Archbishop of Canterbury, as quoted by BBC, 10.4.97)

The 21st century started in the 1970s.
 David Bowie

One can enjoy being taken out to a restaurant so much more, knowing that you're not going to get shagged afterwards.
 Tim Trezare

'How can Truth be described as Gospel?
 Tim Trezare

'Tomorrow' is yesterday's forgotten dream and we must suffer its abandoned promise.
 JAB

"The only reason I speak French is so that I can insult them in their own language and know they won't feel left out."

    Bruen

Matelots Nursery Rhyme
Sing a song of sixpence
A pocket full of rye.
Four and twenty matelots
Baked in a pie.
When the pie was opened
The men cried out in glee.
'We've been twelve years in the Navy
and now were RDP!'

    Barr

William Deihi on 'War' (from '27')

Butchery and boundaries, that's what war is about. There is nothing good or decent or honourable about it. Nothing to be proud of. Nothing heroic or proper. War is the religion of rich men and politicians. It is their church. It is a disgusting enterprise dedicated to the destruction of the young by a bunch of vindictive impotent scabby old men who envy youth. When a war ends we ought to turn the bastards on both sides over to all the blind, legless, armless, and insane leftovers they created. They ought to be flayed skinned alive and burned on the steps of the banks where their profits are stored. Then they should be buried together in common lye-pits, their names struck from all human records and monuments and obliterated from history. And that's better than they deserve.

"It must be pretty lonely being you."
"It is when you're around."
   Anon

US Navy 'pipe':
Sweepers! Sweepers man your brooms.
Sweep from fore to aft,
Bad-guys muster at the Sheriff's office,
Men for liberty fall in by the jolly-boat.'
   Anon

Marriage is an established institution; but who wants to live in an institution?
   Anon

Gabriel Blast: a nasal trumpeting, normally employed at weddings, funerals and state occasions, that secures attention while having little olfactory validity.
   JAB

Pusser's Dunghampers: Naval issue underpants (circa 1950's)

Signal arrives in Omani ship asking that as many people as possible attend a lecture on 'birth spacing'.
Captain: Normally it's nine months but they think they've got it down to eight '

Arab naval officer in wardroom bar
'What ship are you in now?'
'Budweizer!'
   Anon

Topical riddle from May 1997:
Knock, knock.
Who's there?
John!
John who?
It's a tough life in politics.

Admiral's wife to her rugby playing lover while climaxing:
Oh Freddie! Rodney is such a terrible bore. I wish he was into something like you are.
Freddie: Well Dorothy, at this moment, what I'm into is engaged.

   Barr

Only those who know everything can suck the full juice from the marrow of life.

   SL

It is no longer necessary for the poet to write about the breasts of a woman – when he means the bottom of a boy.

   Prince de Limiak

Most children have eye-test-screening at school, but it is very basic and won't pick up things like squints.

   BBC News 22.9.97

Most university students today don't do sex, drugs or learning. They don't even do protesting, like we used to. Now they just do shopping and mobile-phoning.

   GL

The Life and Times of Edwin Cootes (aged eighteen months)
   Chapter 1. God, it's bright out here! Stop hitting me. Why am I hanging upside-down? This is no way to treat a human being.
   Chapter 2. God, I'm hungry! I don't know what it is but the packaging is very attractive. I could get to like this.
   Bruen/Barr

NASSA Professor interviewed on Channel 4 'Equinox' pro-gramme, 27 10 97. "Today we rely much more heavily on satellite technology than we did fifty years ago."

Some 'modern' pronunciations from BBC Radio 4:
   Crinnal justs Sm' (criminal justice system);
   Skoll (Scotland);
   Referendums (referenda);
   Inga (England);
   Pared (period);
   Prilly (probably);
   Sel (cerebral);
   Lon (London);
   Cricking (cricketing);
   Noda (no doubt);
   Premshi (premiership).

Don't tell anyone – or it won't come true.
   TT

We are all inventing our own deaths.
   RR

Why is 'abbreviation' such a long word and how come there is only one Monopolies Commission?

Tim

Today is the tomorrow you worried about yesterday – and all is well.

RR

A neighbour asked if he played the violin – as she often heard him practising.

Classic FM 13 Sept. 1998.

Ride a cock-horse to Banbury Cross,
To see a fine lady ride in a white Porsche.
The ring-road will bring her to the Mall for her clothes,
and she shall have Musak wherever she goes

Bruen

Woman to 8yr old boy in shop
   "I must get some cigarettes for Kathy. Do you know what she smokes?"
   "Marijuana, I think."

People buying newspapers tend to take the second one and leave the top copy. When asked why:
   "There's a small tear in it" or "it has a little mark" and "its wrinkled."

Bruen

Matelots Nursery Rhyme
Humpty Dumpty sat on a wall.
Humpty Dumpty had a great fall.

All the Kings horses and all the Kings men,
were too thick to put him together again.

Barr

With his fastidious expression, the inches of cuff showing from
his jacket sleeves, and the white handkerchief carefully folded
in the breast pocket, 'Delicious Joe' cut a curiously anomalous
figure in the ship's company's dining hall – like a Regency buck
standing in an abattoir.

John Winton HMS Leviathan

Stiggins? It was an impossible name for a Naval Officer. Alfred
Stiggins. He was probably called 'Alfie' in the Squadron. It was a
name for a band-leader: Alfie Stiggins and his Novelty Mando-
liers.

John Winton HMS Leviathan

The pictures, all very modem, suggested framed wallpaper
designs executed by a heroin addict.

(R F Delderfield -. 'The Green Gauntlet')

*Report of the finding of a hijacker's passport in the rubble of the
World Trade Centre.* How did they know? Unless someone
'dropped' it in the 600,000 tons of rubble and then, picking it
up, said, Whose is this I wonder? Al One-way Rashid – must be
a hijacker. What a lucky find!

JB

'The American flag is rapidly becoming a symbol and a rallying
point for the USA'.

Sky News, 17 09 01

Leader of the South Maldon chapter of Animal Liberation
Front to bungling lieutenant:
  You were supposed to target the World Fur Trade – not the
World Trade Fair.

Blessed are they who are stricken only with classifiable diseases.
  Orwell

Parent to child: "How do you know when winter starts?"
Child: "The corner shop starts selling bird-food."

There is no dealing with children, even with children who are
fond of you, unless you can keep your prestige as an adult; let
that prestige be once damaged, and even the best-hearted
children will despise you.
  Orwell

Santa s Reindeer in the 21st century: Rudolph, Spritzer, Blaxo,
Candalene, Zimbabwe, Prozac, Crimpelene, Clandestine,
Bladdleprop, Nomenclature, Prism and Narco-sleepy.
  MAH, JBH, JB, BB

It is always useful to return the rings of dead homing pigeons so
that you know how they were killed, If they were hit by a car or
taken by a hawk, that's OK, but if they just don't come back
then you know not to breed from them.
  Leg O' Mutton pigeon breeder

Blonde twelve-year-old girl to teenage friend: "I'm a trainee-Goth, actually. Every time I go out I wear black eye-shadow."

Granpaw's a-rockin' again. Go get the expired morphine.
  JAR

It is the duty of the old to be anxious for the young and the duty of the young to scorn that anxiety.
  Philip Pullman – 'Northern Lights'

"I very much enjoyed reading your book, Bernie. They broke the mould when they made you."
  ML Director National Marine Aquarium

"The students at Dartmouth study you, Bernie – how to be unorthodoxly successful."
  BRNC Training Commander

'Any (man) who says he enjoys having children is a liar. He might as well say he enjoys being crippled.'
  Anon

For years it used to be said that lifeboats were never lost in the open sea, only on a *bar* when entering or leaving harbour. With modern improvements in design we now lose lifeboats in open water.
  AC Stock – 'Sailing Just for Fun'

Jack Straw (when Foreign Minister): I don' t like to predict things until they have happened.
  Breakfast with Frost, 15 09 02

Private doctor to new mother: "It's a boy, six and a half pounds."
Mother: "You mean guineas, surely?"
  PVB

"There's a shit-load of birds out there, mother. Oh, sorry! Er there's a plethora of ornithological units without."
  MAH 25 12 99

Milk tastes of wood and bread, orange juice of metal mirrors and cars.
  JBH

Explaining why an application for £50,000 to restore the Dunkirk Little Ships was turned down by the National Lottery, the woman responsible said: '...the case was looked at intrinsically not historically and (she was certain) that there must be many similar-design boats of that era still in use.
  BBC News, 28 05 00

I am a politician. I have principles. And if you don t like them, I have others.
  Radio 4, 10 08 00

"I think I'm a pretty positive role-model for kids. I'm not getting drunk every night and shagging lots of men, so if people slag me off, I don't give a shit."
  Victoria 'Posh-Spice' Beckham, Sunday Mirror, 13 08 00

My cousin went to Lourdes and she nearly died of the heat.
  Mrs Ann O'Leary, The Willows, Carngaline, Co Cork.

Royal Mail has decided not to put its image on first class stamps
Instead it will be on the second class stamps.
BBC News, 3 10 00

The firemen s strike is due to start on November 6th – the day
before bonfire night.
BBC News 1.11.02

Boy, cooking breakfast, to mother: "Have you got a knife?"
Mother: "What kind of knife?"
Boy: "A chop-chop knife."
And later: "Have you got a fork?"
Mother: "What kind of fork?"
Boy: "A stab-stab fork."

*What is the difference between a British Cabinet Minister and
a supermarket trolley?*
A supermarket trolley has a mind of its own – but you can get
more food and drink into a Cabinet Minister.
CBFI

The nut-cluster bomb – a hazelnut in every flight.
PVB

*Prime Minister Blair, replying to Parliamentary accusation of
abolishing the 1,400 year old office of Lord Chancellor without
proper debate suggests that:*
"We no longer need a man in full bottom'd wig and women's
tights sitting on a sack of wool as a high official in the land" [He
has now regressed from being a fifth-form prefect to a fourth-
form ink monitor] (18 6 03)

An 'oppo' of mine had never had a girlfriend, then suddenly he had two of them.

I said, "They're like buses."

He said, "Yes, you wait for ages then two come along at once."

I said, "No, they are like buses."

A large woman heard this and remonstrated: "You're fat-ist."

I said, "No, you're fattest."

Snowhite's seven dwarves in the 21st century: Tony, Sleazy, Balti, Druggie, Uni, Pop Idol and Gay *or (through the eyes of an inner city fifteen-year-old)* Faggot, Fuckwit, Piddle, Binger, Wanker, Bollox and Stu.

Fly like a mouse, run like a cushion, be the small bookcase.
  JBH

"Pretty sky; someone sent me a postcard very much like it this Christmas".

  "Did it have a squadron of Dorniers in the top right hand corner, like ours?"

  "No. It didn't."

  "That's where art parts company with reality. Action stations!"

  In Which We Serve

New English in use at the BBC:
  Word-prossa – word processor.
  Genry – gererally.
  Edder – editor.
  Fra – from.

A bit of a damp start to the day with the rain very heavy this morning.

BBC weather forecast, 8.7.03

It is not possible to take seriously any child who cannot get out of bed in the morning. Personal credibility is reduced in direct proportion to the number of hours above eight spent in bed.

As five capital ships, three RFAs and eight coastal vessels gather in Plymouth Sound for review by HM the Queen (in a motor-cutter!), the BBC intones:

'...the biggest gathering of warships at Plymouth for almost a hundred years...' (Hmm... D-Day must have been a pretty small affair then).

"It's a male Common Dolphin and quite healthy. There is nothing wrong with it – apart from its being dead, that is."

BBC News 3/1/04.

Woman, taking part in a BBC phone-in programme concerning the legalization of cannabis, describes how the prescribed use of the substance counteracts a disease of the eye:

"The trouble is that I either cannot see or I am too stoned to know what I am looking at."

"I'd rather play music well than badly; but I'd rather do it badly than not at all."

Derek Bell – The Chieftains

The appeal of Formula One is that it gives you something to watch while you fall asleep.

MAH

Whom the gods love, they would first destroy.
Bruen

Whom God would destroy, he first sends mad.
James Duport

14.6.07 – The Painted Hall, Greenwich
At the end of the Falklands Heroes' Dinner, Margaret Thatcher (Baroness) leaves to a tumultuous ovation that lasted for some minutes. "Maggie and her Beautiful Boys of '82."
PVB

'The Director of MFI has made an unprecedented statement warning us to be aware of terrorist attack.'
'What? I know they reckon to sell bomb-proof furniture but...'
'Did I say MFI? – I meant M15!

The BBC canteen coffee's up to 45p a slice now, we gather.
Ken Bruce

GLENFARG PUDDING
Weigh what number of eggs are necessary for the size of the pudding; take the same weight of sugar, flour and fresh butter. When well mixed, flavour according to taste; put it into a covered mould and steam as long as necessary.
From Lady Landsdowne's War Fund Cookbook, 1900

"All of my life, for the last three years, I have been advocating power-sharing in the Province."
BBC TV Interview with Martin McGuiness 2008

Matelots Nursery Rhyme:
   Mary had a little lamb,
   She also had a hatchet,
   Now she's got a sheepskin coat,
   And a pair of gloves to match it.
   Bruen

The pot of gold is not as valuable as the rainbow that leads to it.
   PVB

Across the Andes by Frog – by Stephen Morris
Chapter 1: God this is an uncomfortable way to travel.
Chapter 2: My frog has collapsed. I can no longer continue.

BBC News/Weather-speak:
   Terror tax – Terrorist attacks.
   Tastrie – Catastrophy.
   Champila – Champion's league.
   Haura – However.
   Tomma – Tomorrow.
   Owlk – Outlook.

And here are some interesting observations:
   Organised rain, reluctant rain, bubbling clouds.
   High pressure building in.
   The breeze will ease away.
   Temperatures topping down to single figures.
   A slow start on the roads on your way to work.
   Gale-Force winds like a hurricane.

Bloody Boomerangs! Can't get rid of 'em!
   JBH

"They genuinely are false tears"
I'm a Celebrity Get Me out of Here 29/11/07

Health Minister interviewed on BBC 2/12/07
"If you ask anybody who has been on dialysis – or even died – they will tell you how dangerous it is to drink raw milk.

"The government is aware of the importance of Parents in bringing up children"
BBC News 11.12.07

Young Omani Girl Guide, asked by examiner in a cookery exam how to tell when the rice was cooked: "The red light goes out"

From an old Indian Army song:
"Across the river lives a boy,
With a bottom like a peach.
Alas, I cannot swim."

Endpiece

Bernie: 'Dickie! My life is a blank canvas.'

Dickie: Well my old mate, my canvas is full and I've got paint left over, do you want some?'

Bernie: 'Cheers Dickie, that would be great!'

Dickie: 'I've only got black left though...'